enter as

CHAMBERS'S
MINERALOGICAL
DICTIONARY

CHAMBERS'S
MINERALOGICAL
DICTIONARY

CHAMBERS'S
MINERALOGICAL
DICTIONARY

With Forty Plates of
COLOURED ILLUSTRATIONS

W. & R. CHAMBERS, LTD.
LONDON AND EDINBURGH

First Published   *1945*
New Edition   *1948*

Printed in Great Britain
by T. and A. Constable Ltd., Hopetoun Street,
Printers to the University of Edinburgh

INDEX TO ILLUSTRATIONS

INDEX TO ILLUSTRATIONS

6

MINERALOGICAL DICTIONARY

A

acanthite. An ore of silver, Ag_2S, crystallising in the orthorhombic system.

accessory minerals. Minerals which occur in small, often minute, amounts in igneous rocks; their presence or absence makes no difference to classification and nomenclature.

achondrite. A type of stony meteorite which compares closely with some basic igneous rocks such as eucrite.

achroite. See TOURMALINE.

acicular. Said of elongated or needle-like crystals.

acmite. An important member of the pyroxene group of minerals, consisting essentially of silicate of iron and sodium, $NaFeSi_2O_6$; occurs in certain alkali-rich igneous rocks.

actinolite. A monoclinic amphibole, containing iron, green in colour, and generally showing an elongated or needle-like habit; occurs in schists and altered basic igneous rocks.

adamantine. Diamond-like. See LUSTRE.

adularescence. A milky or bluish sheen in gemstones.

adularia. See GLASSY FELDSPAR.

aegirine, aegirite. A metasilicate of sodium and iron, occurring commonly in the soda-rich igneous rocks.

aerolites. A general name for stony as distinct from iron meteorites.

agalmatolite. See PAGODITE.

agaric mineral. See ROCK MILK.

agate. This is a cryptocrystalline variety of silica, characterised by parallel, and often curved, bands of colour.

aggregate. A mass consisting of rock or mineral fragments.

alabandite. Massive, granular sulphide of manganese occurring in veins in Rumania and elsewhere. Also called MANGANBLENDE.

alabaster. A massive form of gypsum, pleasingly blotched and stained. On account of its softness it is easily carved and polished, and is widely used for ornamental purposes. Chemically it is $CaSO_4 \cdot 2H_2O$. — ORIENTAL ALABASTER, onyx marble. A beautifully banded form of stalagmitic calcite occurring in Algeria, Egypt, and elsewhere.

albite. The end-member of the plagioclase group of minerals. Ideally consists of silicate of sodium and aluminium; but commonly contains small quantities of potash and lime in addition. Cf. BARBIERITE.

alkali-granite. A coarse-grained (plutonic) rock carrying free quartz and charac-terised by a large excess of alkali-feldspar over plagioclase. In general, the prefix used with a rock name implies a preponderance of soda- or potash-feldspar or feldspathoid over plagioclase.

allanite. A cerium-bearing epidote occurring as an occasional accessory mineral in igneous rocks. Also called ORTHITE.

allemontite. An intergrowth of metallic antimony and arsenic occurring in reniform masses at Allemont (France) and elsewhere.

allotriomorphic. A textural term implying lack of crystal form.

almandine. Iron-aluminium type of garnet, occurring in mica-schists and other metamorphic rocks. Many precious garnets are of this type. Also called ALMANDITE.

almandine spinel. A violet-coloured type of RUBY SPINEL.

alstonite. WITHERITE.

alumina. The trioxide of aluminium, occurring as the mineral CORUNDUM. When the compositions of silicate-minerals are stated in terms of the component oxides, alumina is found to be important in such groups as the feldspars, felspathoids and micas, while augite and hornblende are aluminous, i.e. they contain alumina, probably in solid solution. See also RUBY, SAPPHIRE, EMERY, ORIENTAL AMETHYST.

alunite or **alumstone.** A hydrous sulphate of aluminium and potassium, resulting from the alteration of acid igneous rocks by solfataric action; used in the manufacture of alum.

alunogen. Hydrous sulphate of aluminium, occurring as a white incrustation or efflorescence formed in two different ways: either by volcanic action; or by the decomposition of pyrite (iron-sulphide) in carbonaceous or alum shales.

amalgam. The solution of a metal in mercury: the pasty amalgam of gold and mercury, about one-third gold by weight, obtained from the plates in a mill treating gold ores.

amazonstone, amazonite. A green variety of MICROCLINE, sometimes cut and polished as a gemstone.

amber. This is a fossil resin, found on the shores of the Baltic Sea, containing succinic acid in addition to resin acid and volatile oils. See SUCCINITE.

amblygonite. Fluophosphate of aluminium and lithium, a rare white or greenish mineral, crystallising in the triclinic system.

ambroid. A synthetic amber formed by heating and compressing pieces of natural amber too small to be of value in themselves. Also known as AMBEROID and PRESSED AMBER.

amethyst. A clear mauve-coloured form of quartz, used as a semi-precious gemstone.—ORIENTAL AMETHYST. See FALSE AMETHYST.

amianthus. A fine, silky variety of asbestos.

amphiboles. An important group of dark-coloured, rock-forming silicates, including hornblende, the commonest.

amphibolite. A crystalline, coarse-grained rock, containing amphibole as an essential constituent, together with feldspar and frequently garnet; like hornblende-schist, formed by regional metamorphism of basic igneous rocks, but not foliated.

amygdale, amygdule. An almond-shaped infilling (by secondary minerals such as agate, zeolites, calcite, etc.) of elongated steam cavities in igneous rocks.

analcine, analcite. A zeolite; important hydrated silicate of aluminium and sodium, closely related to albite but containing less silica.

anatase. One of the three naturally occurring forms of crystalline titanium dioxide, of tabular or bipyramidal habit. See also OCTAHEDRITE.

andalusite. One of the three different crystalline forms of aluminium silicate; a characteristic product of the contact metamorphism of argillaceous rocks.

andesine. A member of the plagioclase group of minerals, with a small excess of soda over lime; typical of the intermediate igneous rocks.

andesite. A fine-grained igneous rock (usually a lava), of intermediate composition, having plagioclase as the dominant feldspar.

andradite. Common calcium-iron garnet. Includes melanite (black garnet), though all andradite is not black.

anglesite. Orthorhombic sulphate of lead—a common lead ore; named after the original locality, Anglesey.

anhydrite. Anhydrous calcium sulphate; alters readily into gypsum.

ankerite. A carbonate of calcium, magnesium, and iron. Frequently associated with iron ores.

annabergite. Hydrous nickel arsenate, apple-green monoclinic crystals, rare, usually massive. Associated with other ores of nickel. Also called NICKEL BLOOM.

anomite. A form of biotite, identical with the latter in all characters but optical orientation.

anorthic system. A style of crystal architecture now commonly termed TRICLINIC SYSTEM (q.v.).

anorthite. The lime-rich end-member of the plagioclase feldspar group of minerals; silicate of calcium and aluminium, occurring in some igneous rocks, typically in those produced by the contact metamorphism of impure calcareous sediments. Also called INDIANITE.

anorthoclase. A cryptoperthitic soda-potash feldspar, characterised by a blue play of colour in the hand specimen; occurs typically in the soda-syenite, laurvikite, from S. Norway, which is largely used for facing buildings in this country and elsewhere.

anthophyllite. An orthorhombic amphibole of grey-brown colour, usually massive, and normally occurring in metamorphic rocks; a metasilicate of magnesium and iron.

anthracite. A hard, slow-burning variety of coal, yielding very little ash, moisture, and volatiles; generally used in closed stoves, calorific value per pound, about 14,900 B.Th.U.

antigorite. A lamellar form of SERPENTINE, the type locality being the Antigorio valley, Piedmont.

antimonial lead. Native lead containing small amounts of antimony and crystallising in the cubic system.

antimonite. (1) STIBNITE. — (2) Several minerals are antimonites in the chemical sense, e.g. ROMEITE.

antimony. A native metallic element, white with a bluish tinge; symbol Sb; at. wt. 121·76; at. no. 51; sp. gr. at 20° C., 6·62; m.p. 630° C.; b.p. 1440° C. Specific electrical resistivity, 39 microhms per cm. cub. The native metal occurs either in rhombohedral crystals, in granular or lamellar masses, or in shapeless masses.

antimony glance. An obsolete name for stibnite.

apatite. Naturally occurring phosphate of calcium, with chloride or fluoride of calcium, occurring widely distributed in igneous rocks in the form of hexagonal crystals, usually of very small size.

apophyllite. A secondary mineral (remarkable for the size and perfection of its crystals) occurring with the zeolites in geodes in decomposed basalts and other igneous rocks. Composition: hydrated silicate of potassium and calcium. Also called FISH-EYE.

aquamarine. A variety of BERYL of pale yellowish-green, bluish-green or sea-green colour; used as a gemstone.

aragonite. The relatively unstable, ortho-rhombic form of the dimorphous crystalline calcium carbonate, deposited from warm water, but prone to inversion into calcite. See also FLOS FERRI.

argentiferous galena. See SILVER LEAD ORE.

argentiferous lead. Lead which contains silver.

argentite. An important ore of silver, having the composition Ag_2S (silver sulphide); occurs as cubic crystals. Also called SILVER GLANCE.

argillaceous rocks. Sedimentary rocks of the clay grade, i.e. composed of minute mineral fragments and crystals less than 0·002 mm. in diameter, also much colloidal material. Apart from finely divided detrital matter, they consist essentially of the so-called clay minerals, such as montmorillonite, kaolinite, gibbsite, and diaspore.

Arizona ruby. A pyrope from Arizona.

arquerite. See SILVER AMALGAM.

arsenic. Symbol, As. At. wt. 74·91, at. no. 33, valencies 3, 5. An element which occurs free and combined in a large number of minerals. Described as grey or γ-arsenic to distinguish it from the other allotropic modifications. M.p. 814° C. (36 atm.), b.p. 615° C. (sublimes), sp. gr. 5·73 at 15° C.

arsenical nickel. NICCOLITE.

arsenical pyrite or **arsenopyrite.** See MISPICKEL.

arsenolite. Arsenic trioxide, a decomposition product of arsenical ores; occurring commonly as a white incrustation, rarely as fibrous cubic crystals.

artificial stones. Gemstones manufactured by man, not by nature. The term includes reconstructed stones made by fusing together small crystals or fragments; synthetic stones of composition and physical characters identical with those of the natural stones; and imitation stones (paste) resembling true minerals in superficial appearance only. Some experts restrict the term to the last-named category.

asbestos. Two different mineral species are included under this term: (a) amphibole, ranging in composition from tremolite to actinolite; and (b) a form of serpentine. Both types of asbestos occur in veins as fibrous crystals, so extremely thin as to be elastic and capable, in some cases, of being woven into fabric. Withstands high temperatures without change, and hence used in making fireproof materials of many kinds.

asbolane. A form of WAD—soft, earthy manganese dioxide, containing up to about 32% of cobalt oxide. Also ASBOLITE.

asparagus stone. Apatite of a yellowish-green colour, especially specimens from the original locality, Marcia (Spain).

asphalt. This is a bituminous deposit formed in oil-bearing strata by the removal, usually through evaporation, of the volatiles. Occurs in the ‘tar pools’ of California and elsewhere and in the pitch lake in Trinidad, whence enormous quantities are exported.

asterism. A light effect due to the presence of minute, almost ultramicroscopic, inclusions arranged in parallel series in some varieties of ruby, sapphire, and phlogopite mica. A point source of light viewed through a plate of this form of phlogopite appears as a light star.

atacamite. A green hydrated chloride of copper, widely distributed in S. America, Australia, India, etc.; occurring also at St Just (Cornwall).

augite. An aluminous silicate of calcium, iron and magnesium (pyroxene group),

crystallising in the monoclinic system, and occurring in many igneous rocks, particularly those of basic composition; it is an essential constituent of basalt, dolerite, and gabbro.

australites. See TEKTITES.

autunite. Hydrous phosphate of calcium and uranium, resembling torbernite, but yellow.

aventurine feldspar. A variety of sodic oligoclase, near albite in composition, characterised by minute disseminated particles of red iron oxide which cause fire-like flashes of colour. Also called SUNSTONE.

aventurine quartz. A form of quartz charged, sometimes densely, with minute inclusions of either mica or iron oxide. Used in ornamental jewellery.

axinite. A complex borosilicate of calcium and aluminium, with varying small quantities of iron and manganese, produced by pneumatolysis and occurring as brown wedge-shaped triclinic crystals.

azure quartz. See SAPPHIRE QUARTZ.

azurite. One of the basic carbonates of copper, occurring either as deep-blue monoclinic crystals or as kidney-like masses built of closely packed radiating fibres. Also called CHESSYLITE (from Chessy, in France). Cf. MALACHITE.

B

balas ruby. RUBY SPINEL.

ball-jasper. Jasper showing a concentric banding of red and yellow.

ballas. Industrial diamond. See BORT.

banket. Originally denoted gold-bearing conglomerates of the Witwatersrand, consisting of quartz pebbles cemented by a siliceous material. It is now used more widely for similar conglomerates and conglomeratic quartzites.

barbierite. A feldspar of the composition of ALBITE, but crystallising in the monoclinic system.

barytes or **barite.** Native BARIUM SULPHATE, BaSO₄, typically showing tabular orthorhombic crystals. It is a common veinstone in association with lead ores, and occurs also as nodules in limestone and in the fuller's earth beds of Surrey; also locally as a cement of sandstones. Sp. gr. 4·5; hence called HEAVY SPAR.

barytocalcite. A double carbonate of calcium and barium, CaCO₃·BaCO₃, crystallising on the monoclinic system, and occurring typically in lead veins.

basalt. A fine-grained, often porphyritic (see PORPHYRITIC TEXTURE), igneous rock of dark colour, composed essentially of basic plagioclase feldspar and pyroxene, with or without olivine.

bastite. A variety of serpentine, essentially hydrated silicate of magnesium, resulting from the alteration of orthorhombic pyroxenes. It occurs in the serpentine of Baste in the Harz mountains, also in the Cornish and other serpentines. Also known as SCHILLERSPAR.

bauxite. A residual clay, consisting essentially of aluminium hydroxides, formed in tropical regions by the chemical weathering of basic igneous rocks. It is the most important ore of aluminium. Extensive deposits occur in British and Dutch Guiana, northern France, and in many other localities. In U.S.A. bauxite of commercial value is restricted to Arkansas and the southern Appalachian states, e.g. at Rock Run, Alabama. See also LATERITE.

bell-metal ore. See STANNITE.

benitoite. A strongly dichroic mineral, varying in tint from sapphire blue to colourless, discovered in San Benito Co., California. Silicate of barium and titanium.

bentonite. A valuable clay, similar in its properties to fuller's earth, formed by the decomposition of volcanic glass, under water. Consists largely of montmorillonite.

beryl. This is a silicate of beryllium and aluminium, occurring in pegmatites as beautiful hexagonal crystals of blue, yellow, or pink colour. Used as gemstones.

betafite. A hydrous columbate, niobate, and titanate of uranium; a radioactive mineral, described from Betafo in Madagascar.

billitonites. See TEKTITES.

biotite. A member of the mica group, widely distributed in igneous rocks (particularly in granites) as lustrous black crystals, with a singularly perfect cleavage. In composition, it is a complex silicate, chiefly of iron and magnesium, together with potassium.

bipyramid. A crystal form consisting of two pyramids on a common base, the one being the mirror-image of the other.

bismite. See BISMUTH OCHRE.

bismuth. Symbol, Bi. A greyish-white metallic element in the fifth group of the periodic system. At. no. 83, at. wt. 209·0, sp. gr. 9·72-9·88.

bismuth glance. See BISMUTHINITE.

bismuth ochre. Trioxide of bismuth, occurring as shapeless masses or as an earthy deposit. Also called BISMITE.

bismuthinite. Sulphide of bismuth, Bi_2S_3, rarely forming crystals, commonly occurring in shapeless lead-grey masses with a yellowish tarnish. Also called BISMUTH GLANCE.

bismutite. An amorphous form of bismuth carbonate, occurring as a rare natural mineral.

bisphenoid. A crystal form consisting of four faces of triangular shape, two meeting at the top and two at the base in chisel-like edges, at right-angles to one another; hence the name, meaning 'double edged.'

bitter spar. DOLOMITE.

bitumen. A name applied by different scientists to some or all of a number of closely related inflammable mineral substances, including ASPHALT. All consist mainly of carbon and hydrogen and are thought to be of vegetable origin. See ASPHALT.

black-band iron-ore. A carbonaceous variety of clay-ironstone, the iron being present as carbonate — chalybite (or siderite); occurs in the English Coal Measures.

black diamond. A variety of crystalline carbon, related to diamond, but showing no crystal form. Highly prized, on account of its hardness, as an abrasive. Occurs only in Brazil. Also called CARBONADO.

black jack. See BLENDE.

black lava glass. See OBSIDIAN.

black lead. A commercial form of GRAPHITE.

black opal. Opals of dark tint are so called, though they are rarely black; the fine Australian blue opal, with flame-coloured flashes, is typical. See OPAL.

blende or **zinc blende.** Zinc sulphide, the chief ore of zinc, occurring in metalliferous veins in association with galena, etc. Crystallises in cubic system. Also called BLACK JACK, SPHALERITE (esp. U.S.).

bloodstone. Cryptocrystalline silica, a variety of chalcedony, coloured deep-green, with flecks of red jasper; often used in signet rings. Also called HELIOTROPE.

blue asbestos. A form of crocidolite, silicate of sodium and iron, occurring in Asbestos Mountains (Griqualand West, S. Africa) and (rarely) elsewhere.

blue ground. Decomposed agglomerate, occurring in volcanic pipes in S. Africa and Brazil; it contains a remarkable assemblage of ultra-basic plutonic rock-fragments (many of large size) and diamonds.

blue john. A massive or fibrous, frequently banded, purplish variety of the mineral fluorite occurring typically in Derbyshire.

blue vitriol. See CHALCANTHITE.

Bobrovska garnet. See URALIAN EMERALD.

bog iron-ore. Hydrated iron-oxide deposited in marshy places, perhaps by the action of iron bacteria.

bog oak. Oak immersed in peat bogs, semi-fossilised and blackened to resemble ebony by iron from the water combining with the tannin of the oak.

Bohemian ruby. Not ruby at all but the much less valuable mineral ROSE QUARTZ.

Bohemian topaz. See CITRINE.

bone turquoise. Fossil bone or tooth, coloured blue with phosphate of iron; widely used in the past and at present as a gemstone. It is not true turquoise, and loses its colour in the course of time. Also called ODONTOLITE.

boracite. The cubic, or pseudocubic, form of magnesium borate, together with magnesium chloride. found in beds of gypsum and anhydrite, e.g. at Stassfurt in Germany.

borax. A mineral deposited by evaporation of the waters of alkaline lakes, notably in California, Nevada, and Tibet. Borax, which is hydrated sodium borate, occurs as a surface efflorescence, or as monoclinic crystals embedded in the lacustrine mud.

bornite. A valuable copper ore, a sulphide of copper and iron, Cu_3FeS_3, cubic crystals; occurs in Cornwall and elsewhere.

bort. (1) The bort of commerce is often the splinters, rough fragments, and imperfect crystals of ordinary diamonds; (2) 'ballas bort,' a finely crystalline form of carbon, occurring in small spherical bodies showing an internal radiating structure. Possessing the hardness of diamond, bort is exceedingly tough, and is used as the boring agent in rock drills.

botryoidal. Like a bunch of grapes.

boule. A small pear-shaped mass of synthetic sapphire, ruby, etc., produced by the fusion of alumina, suitably tinted, in a furnace of special design.

bournonite. An orthorhombic sulphide of lead, copper and antimony, occurring commonly in wheel-shaped twins. Called also WHEEL ORE.

bowenite. A compact, finely granular, massive form of serpentine, formerly thought to be nephrite, and used for the same purposes.

bowlingite. See SAPONITE.

braunite. A massive, or occasionally well-crystallised, cubic ore of manganese, occurring in India, New South Wales, and several European localities. Composition $3Mn_2O_3 \cdot MnSiO_3$.

Brazilian emerald. A pure-green, deeply coloured variety of tourmaline, occurring in Brazil; used as a gemstone.

Brazilian pebble. The name applied to Brazilian quartz or rock-crystal, used in the manufacture of spheres for crystal-gazing, lenses, etc.

Brazilian peridot. Green crystals from Brazil having the typical colour of peridot (olivine); they are probably specimens of chrysoberyl.

Brazilian ruby. Among the many coloured topaz crystals mined in Brazil some are pink (rose topaz), others deep red; these latter are termed *Brazilian ruby.*

Brazilian sapphire. A trade name for the beautiful clear blue variety of tourmaline mined in Brazil; used as a gemstone.

brilliant. The name applied to a diamond when cut and polished for use as a gemstone in the form generally adopted; i.e. with a large face (known as the *table*) girdled by 33 facets in the *crown*, and having a further 25 facets in the *pavilion* (the part of the stone below the *girdle*).

Bristol diamonds. Small lustrous crystals of quartz, i.e. rock crystal, occurring in the Bristol district.

brittle micas. A group of minerals (the clintonite group) resembling the true micas in crystallographic characters, but having the cleavage flakes less elastic. Chemically, they are distinguished by containing calcium as an essential constituent.

brittle silver ore. A popular name for STEPHANITE.

brochantite. A basic sulphate of copper occurring in fibrous masses, or as incrustations; formed by the decomposition of chalcopyrite.

bronzite. One of the orthopyroxenes, near hypersthene in composition; characterised by a metallic sheen, due to the reflection of light from planes of minute metallic inclusions in the surface layers.

brookite. A form of crystalline titanium dioxide, occurring in flat, red-brown, platy, orthorhombic crystals.

brown coal or **lignite.** Intermediate between peat and true coals, with a high moisture content, the calorific value per pound about 4000 to 5000 B.Th.U.; used for firing boilers; found almost exclusively in Germany. The hydrogenation of brown coal is of great importance for the production of synthetic fuel, lubricating oils, and motor spirit.

brown haematite. A misnomer; the mineral bearing this name is LIMONITE, a hydrous iron-oxide, whereas true haematite is anhydrous.

brown iron-ore. See LIMONITE.

brown lead-ore. See PYROMORPHITE.

brucite. Hydroxide of magnesium, occurring as fibrous masses in serpentines. See also PERICLASE.

brucite-marble. A product of dedolomitisation; a crystalline metamorphic rock formed by the action of intense heat on dolomitic (or magnesian) limestone.

buchite. A glassy rock resulting from the fusion of clay or shale, following its incorporation in magma. Crystals and microlites are normally present.

burmite. An amber-like mineral occurring in the upper Hukong Valley, Burma, differing from ordinary amber by containing no succinic acid.

butter-rock. See HALOTRICHITE.

bytownite. A variety of plagioclase feldspar, containing a high proportion of the anorthite molecule.

C

cairngorm. Smoky-yellow or brown varieties of quartz, the colouring matter probably due to some organic compound; named from Cairngorm in the Scottish Grampians, the more attractively coloured varieties being used as semi-precious gemstones. Also called SMOKY QUARTZ.

calamine. (1) In England, smithsonite; (2) in U.S.A., hemimorphite (*electric calamine*).

calcite or **calcspar.** One of the dimorphous forms of calcium carbonate, showing trigonal symmetry and a great variety of mineral habits. It is one of the commonest of minerals in association with both igneous and sedimentary rocks.

calcium carbonate. See CALCITE, ARAGONITE.

calcium fluoride. See FLUORSPAR.
,, **phosphate.** See APATITES.
,, **silicate.** See WOLLASTONITE.
,, **sulphate.** See GYPSUM.
,, **titanate.** See PEROVSKITE.
,, **tungstate.** See SCHEELITE.

calco-uranite. See AUTUNITE.

calc-spar. See CALCITE.

caliche. See SODA NITRE.

Californian jade. A compact form of green vesuvianite (idiocrase) obtained from California, and used as an ornamental stone and in jewellery. Also known as CALIFORNITE.

Californian onyx. A term wrongly applied to amber- or brown-tinted aragonite, a soft mineral unsuited for use as a cut stone.

callainite. A very rare green phosphate of aluminium, resembling turquoise but translucent.

campylite. See KAMPYLITE.

Canadian asbestos. See CHRYSOTILE.

cannel coal. A dull variety of coal, breaking with a conchoidal fracture; it is rich in volatile constituents, and burns with a bright flame.

Cape asbestos or Cape blue asbestos. A form of crocidolite, a silicate of sodium and iron, occurring in narrow interbedded veins traversing the Griqua Town series of banded jaspers and ironstones in Griqualand West, Union of S. Africa.

Cape ruby. The fiery red garnet PYROPE obtained in the diamond-mines in the Kimberley district, mostly from the rocks kimberlite and eclogite.

capillary pyrite. See MILLERITE.

carat. (1) A standard of weight for precious stones. The *metric carat*, standardised in 1932, equals 200 mg. and so is a little smaller than the older British carat.—(2) The standard of fineness for gold. The standard for pure gold is 24 carats; 22 carat gold has 2 parts of alloy; 18 carat gold 6 parts of alloy.

carbonado. See BLACK DIAMOND.

carbuncle. This is the precious garnet; it consists of an iron-aluminium-silicate, which crystallises in the cubic system. It has a deep-red colour. See ALMANDINE.

carnallite. The hydrated chloride of potassium and magnesium, crystallising in the orthorhombic system; occurring in bedded masses with other saline deposits, as at Stassfurt. Such deposits arise from the desiccation of salt-lakes. It is used as a fertiliser.

carnelian. See CORNELIAN.

carrollite. A sulphide of cobalt, with small amounts of copper, iron, and nickel; crystallises in the cubic system.

cassiterite or tin-stone. The dioxide of tin, crystallising in the tetragonal system; it constitutes the most important ore of this metal. It occurs in veins and impregnations associated with granitic rocks; also as 'stream-tin' in alluvial gravels.

cat sapphire. Blackish- or greenish-blue oriental sapphire (i.e. true sapphire) of some value as a cut gemstone, but not of characteristic colour.

cat's-eye. This is a variety of fibrous quartz which shows chatoyancy when suitably cut, as an ornamental stone. The term is also applied to crocidolite when infiltrated with silica (see TIGER'S EYE, HAWK'S EYE). A more valuable form is CHRYSOBERYL CAT'S-EYE. See CYMOPHANE.

celestine. A name for strontium sulphate, crystallising in the orthorhombic system; occurs in association with rock-salt and gypsum; also in the sulphur deposits of Sicily, and in nodules in limestone. The main supply for the world's markets is from residual clays. Also CELESTITE.

cerargyrite. Silver chloride, crystallising in the cubic system. It is usually the product of secondary action, and occurs commonly in massive or wax-like forms, associated with native silver or silver ores. Also CHLORARGYRITE, HORNSILVER.

cerussite. White lead ore, lead carbonate, crystallising in the orthorhombic system; it occurs in association with other lead ores.

Ceylonese chrysolite. Trade name for fine golden-yellow CHRYSOBERYL.

Ceylonese peridot. The trade name for a yellowish-green variety of the mineral tourmaline, approaching olivine in colour; used as a semi-precious gemstone.

Ceylonese ruby. True ruby does occur, rather rarely, in Ceylon, together with much commoner ruby-spinel. Much of the gemstone material sold under this name is spinel.

Ceylonese zircon. True zircon occurs in Ceylon, but frequently this is not differentiated from tourmaline of the same colour. *Ceylonian* (sic) *zircon* is the name given by jewellers to the fire-red, yellow, yellowish-green, and grey zircons.

ceylonite. See PLEONASTE.

chabazite. This is a hydrated silicate of aluminium, calcium, and potassium, crystallising in the trigonal system (rhombohedral habit) and belonging to the zeolite group.

chalcanthite. Hydrated copper sulphate, $CuSO_4 \cdot 5H_2O$, crystallising in the triclinic system; it occurs as an alteration product of copper pyrite and other copper ores. Popularly called BLUE VITRIOL.

chalcedony. A cryptocrystalline variety of silica, possibly to be regarded as a mixture of crystalline and amorphous silica. It occurs filling cavities in lavas, or associated with flint.

chalcocite. A greyish-black metallic sulphide of copper, Cu_2S, which crystallises in the orthorhombic system; it occurs in veins and beds with other copper ores, but is not very abundant. Also called COPPER GLANCE, REDRUTHITE.

chalcopyrite or **copper pyrite.** Sulphide of copper and iron, crystallising in the tetragonal system; the commonest ore of copper, occurring in mineral veins. The crystals are brassy yellow, often showing superficial tarnish or iridescence.

chalcostibite. Sulphide of copper and antimony, occurring in the orthorhombic system. Also WOLFSBERGITE.

chalcotrichite. A red, semi-translucent variety of CUPRITE, characterised by its capillary habit.

chalybite. Carbonate of iron, crystallising in the trigonal system (rhombohedral habit). It occurs in an impure form as beds and nodules (clay-ironstone), as well as in crystal aggregates in mineral veins. It is an ore of iron. Also called SIDERITE, SPATHIC IRON.

chamosite. A silicate of iron occurring in oölitic and other bedded iron ores.

chatoyancy. The characteristic optical effect shown by cat's-eye and certain other minerals, due to the reflection of light from minute aligned tubular channels, perhaps 25,000 to the square cm. When cut *en cabochon* such stones exhibit a narrow silvery band of light which changes its position as the gem is turned.

chert. A siliceous rock consisting of cryptocrystalline silica, and sometimes including the remains of siliceous organisms, such as sponges or radiolaria.

chessylite. See AZURITE.

chiastolite or **cross-stone.** A variety of andalusite occurring in metamorphic rocks; characterised by cruciform inclusions of carbonaceous matter.

Chile nitre, Chile saltpetre. A commercial name for sodium nitrate, $NaNO_3$.

china clay. A hydrated silicate of aluminium, resulting from the decomposition of the feldspars in igneous rocks by pneumatolysis. It contains a high percentage of aluminium silicate —$Al_2O_3 \cdot 2SiO_2 \cdot 2H_2O$—and is of great value in ceramic industry. Also called KAOLIN, PORCELAIN CLAY. See also KAOLINITE.

chinastone. A kaolinitised granitic rock containing unaltered plagioclase. Also applied to certain limestones of exceptionally fine grain and smooth texture.

chloanthite, cloanthite. Arsenide of nickel, $NiAs_2$, occurring in the cubic system. This is a valuable nickel ore, often associated with smaltite.

chlor-apatite. See APATITE.

chlorargyrite. Chloride of silver occurring in cubic crystals; usually associated with native silver.

chlorastrolite. A green mineral of fibrous habit resembling prehnite; it occurs in rounded geodes in basic igneous rocks near Lake Superior. When cut *en cabochon* it exhibits chatoyancy and is used as a semi-precious gemstone.

chlorites. A group of allied minerals which may be regarded as hydrated silicates of aluminium, iron, and magnesium. They crystallise in the monoclinic system, and are of green colour. They occur as alteration products of such minerals as biotite and hornblende, and also in schistose rocks.

chlorite schist. A schist composed largely of the mineral chlorite, in association with quartz, epidote, etc. Formed from igneous rock by dynamothermal metamorphism.

chlorophaeite. A mineral closely related to chlorite, dark-green when fresh, but rapidly changing to brown, hence the name (Greek *chloros*, yellowish-green, *phaios*, dun). Described from basic igneous rocks.

chondrite. A type of stony meteorite containing *chondrules* — nodule-like aggregates of minerals.

chrome iron ore. See CHROMITE.

chrome spinel. Another name for the mineral PICOTITE, a member of the spinel group.

chromite. A double oxide of chromium and iron, used as a source of chromium; a member of the spinel group. Chromite occurs as an accessory in some basic and ultrabasic rocks, and crystallises in the cubic system as lustrous grey-black octahedra; also massive. Also called CHROME IRON ORE.

chrysoberyl. Aluminate of beryllium, crystallising in the orthorhombic system. The crystals often have a stellate habit and are green to yellow in colour. In the gemstone trade yellow chrysoberyl is known as *chrysolite*.

chrysoberyl cat's eye. See CYMOPHANE.

chrysolite. The mineralogical name for common OLIVINE, sometimes restricted to the pale-yellowish crystals of gemstone quality. The term is incorrectly applied to chrysoberyl of golden-yellow colour.

chrysoprase. A pale apple-green variety of chalcedony; the pigmentation is probably due to the oxide of nickel.

chrysotile. A fibrous variety of serpentine, occurring in small veins. It forms part of the asbestos of commerce. Also called CANADIAN ASBESTOS.

cinnabar. This is sulphide of mercury, HgS, occurring as red acicular crystals, or massive; the ore of mercury, worked extensively at Almadén, Spain, and elsewhere.

cinnamon stone. See HESSONITE.

citrine or **quartz topaz** or **false topaz.** Not the true TOPAZ (q.v.) of mineralogists, but a yellow variety of quartz, which closely resembles it in colour though not in other physical characters; it is of much less value than true topaz. It figures under a variety of geographical names; e.g. BOHEMIAN TOPAZ, INDIAN TOPAZ, MADAGASCAR TOPAZ, MADEIRA TOPAZ, and SPANISH TOPAZ (q.v.). See also SCOTCH

TOPAZ, SMOKY QUARTZ. BRAZILIAN TOPAZ is the true mineral.

clay. A fine-textured, sedimentary, or residual deposit. It consists of hydrated silicates of aluminium mixed with various impurities.

clay ironstone. Nodular beds of clay and iron compounds, often associated with the Coal Measure rocks.

cleavage. (1) The splitting of a crystal along certain planes parallel to certain actual or possible crystal faces, when subjected to tension.—(2) A property of rocks, such as slates, whereby they can be split into thin sheets. Cleavage is produced by intense pressures due to earth movement, and the cleavage planes are commonly highly inclined to the direction of the pressure which produced them.

Cleveland iron ore. An ironstone consisting of iron carbonate, which occurs in the Middle Lias rocks of North Yorkshire near Middlesbrough. The ironstone is oölitic and yields on the average 30% iron.

clinochlore. RIPIDOLITE.

cloanthite. See CHLOANTHITE.

coal. A general name for firm brittle carbonaceous rocks; derived from vegetable debris, but altered, particularly in respect of volatile constituents, by pressure, earth movements, and a variety of other chemical processes.

cobalt bloom. See ERYTHRITE.

cobalt glance. See COBALTITE.

cobaltiferous wad. An impure hydrated oxide of manganese containing up to 30% of cobalt.

cobaltite. Sulphide and arsenide of cobalt, crystallising in the cubic system; usually found massive and compact with smaltite. Also called COBALT GLANCE.

cock's comb pyrites. SPEAR PYRITES, a form of MARCASITE.

colemanite. Hydrated calcium borate, crystallising in the monoclinic system; occurs as nodules in clay found in California and elsewhere.

Colorado ruby. An incorrect name for the fiery-red garnet (pyrope) crystals obtained from Colorado and certain other parts of U.S.A.

Colorado topaz. True topaz of a brownish-yellow colour is obtained in Colorado, but quartz similarly coloured is sometimes sold under the same name.

coloradoite. Mercuric telluride, crystallising in the cubic system. It usually occurs in the massive state.

columbite or niobite. A niobate and tantalate of iron and manganese, crystallising in the orthorhombic system. It occurs in granitoid rocks, and is the chief source of tantalum.

columnar crystals. Elongated crystals formed by growth taking place at right-angles to the surface of the mould.

compact. If the crystalline grains in a structure can be detected only by the high powers of a microscope, the structure is called COMPACT, and the mineral MASSIVE. Cf. CRYPTOCRYSTALLINE.

conchoidal fracture. Substances like quartz break with smooth rounded surfaces, broken by curved lines like the lines of growth on a shell. This is called *conchoidal fracture.*

cooperite. Sulphide and arsenide of platinum, crystallising in the orthorhombic system. It occurs in minute and irregular grains in igneous rocks.

copalite or copaline. A pale-yellow waxy substance, found in the London Clay at Highgate. Also called HIGHGATE RESIN.

copals. A class of natural resins of recent or recent-fossil origin, consisting of resin acids, resenes, and essential oils. They furnish raw material for the varnish and linoleum industries. Important copals are Congo, dammar, kauri, Zanzibar, amber, and others.

copper carbonate. See AZURITE and MALACHITE.

copper glance. See CHALCOCITE.

copper, native. Like those of gold and silver, crystals of copper are of the cubic system, but well-shaped cubes are quite exceptional, and even complex crystals are rare. The metal has usually the form of thin plates filling narrow crevices in igneous rocks or slate or sandstone; these are often dendritic. Mossy aggregates are also common, particularly in the upper parts of veins of copper ore. Native copper is usually dull and tarnished. It is seldom in sufficient quantity to be worked.

copper nickel. See NICCOLITE.

copper ores. See CHALCOPYRITE, ATACAMITE, AZURITE, TORBERNITE, LINARITE, MALACHITE, TETRAHEDRITE.

copper oxide. See CUPRITE.

copper pyrite. See CHALCOPYRITE.

copper sulphate. See CHALCANTHITE.

copper uranite. See TORBERNITE.

copperas. Iron sulphate, $FeSO_4 \cdot 7H_2O$. See MELANTERITE.

copperas, white. GOSLARITE.

cordierite. A silicate of aluminium, iron, and magnesium with water, which crystallises in the orthorhombic system; occurs chiefly in metamorphic rocks. Also called IOLITE and DICHROITE.

cornelian. A translucent red variety of CHALCEDONY.

Cornish 'diamond.' Like other 'diamonds' prefixed by a place name, this is merely clear crystalline quartz.

corundum. Name for oxide of aluminium, crystallising in the trigonal system. It is next to diamond in hardness, and hence is used as an abrasive. See also WHITE SAPPHIRE.

covellite. Sulphide of copper crystallising in the hexagonal system, usually occurring as thin plates. The colour is indigo-blue or darker. Also called INDIGO COPPER.

cristobalite. Silica which crystallises in white octahedra. This is a high-temperature modification of quartz, being formed above 1470° C. It may have two varieties, one tetragonal and the other cubic.

crocidolite. A dark-blue silicate of sodium and iron, crystallising in the monoclinic system and belonging to the amphibole group of rock-forming minerals. Usually considered to be a fibrous variety of riebeckite. See also TIGER'S EYE.

crocoite or **crocoisite.** Chromate of lead, crystallising in the monoclinic system, $PbCrO_4$; bright-red in colour.

crookesite. Selenide of copper and thallium, often with 1%-5% silver. It is massive and compact, and displays metallic lustre.

cross-stone. See CHIASTOLITE.

cryolite. Fluoride of aluminium and sodium, Na_3AlF_6, crystallising in the monoclinic system. It usually occurs as a vein in granite rocks, and is used in the manufacture of aluminium and white porcellanous glass. Also called GREEN-LAND SPAR.

cryptocrystalline. Consisting of very minute crystals.

crystal. A body, generally solid, whose atoms are arranged in a definite pattern, the crystal faces being an outward expression of the regular arrangement of the atoms. In the case of small and undistorted crystals each face is an optically plane surface. A *cleavage face* is the smooth surface resulting from cleavage; in such minerals as mica, the cleavage face may be almost a plane surface, diverging only by the thickness of a molecule.

crystal systems. A classification of crystals based on the intercepts made on the crystallographic axes by certain planes.

crystal texture. The size and arrangement of the individual crystals in a crystalline mass.

crystalline form. The external geometrical shape of a crystal.

crystallites. Very small, imperfectly formed crystals. Also minute bodies occurring in glassy igneous rocks, and marking a stage in incipient crystallisation.

cubic system. The crystal system which has the highest degree of symmetry; it embraces such forms as the cube and octahedron.

cupid's darts. See FLÈCHES D'AMOUR.

cupriferous pyrite. See CHALCOPYRITE.

cuprite. Oxide of copper, crystallising in the cubic system. It is usually red in colour and often occurs associated with native copper; a common ore.

cupro-uranite. See TORBERNITE.

cyanite. See KYANITE.

cylindrite. A complex sulphide of lead, tin, antimony, which has a cylindrical habit. The crystal system is not known for certain.

cymophane. A variety of the gem-mineral *chrysoberyl* which exhibits chatoyancy; sometimes known as CHRYSOBERYL CAT'S-EYE or ORIENTAL CAT'S-EYE.

D

danaite. A variety of MISPICKEL in which 5 to 10 per cent. of the iron is replaced by cobalt.

danburite. A rare accessory mineral, occurring in pegmatites as yellow orthorhombic crystals. Chemically, danburite is a calcium borosilicate, $CaB_2Si_2O_8$.

datolite. A hydrated silicate of boron and calcium occurring as a secondary product in amygdales and veins, usually as distinct prismatic monoclinic crystals.

dechenite. A rare mineral usually occurring in nodular aggregates; chemically, vanadate of lead.

dedolomitisation. The recrystallisation of a dolomite rock or dolomitic limestone consequent on contact metamorphism; essentially involving the breaking down of the dolomite into its two components, $CaCO_3$ and $MgCO_3$. The former merely recrystallises into a coarse calcite mosaic; but the latter breaks down further into MgO and CO_2. The magnesium oxide may occur in the rock as periclase, more commonly as brucite, while in the presence of silica magnesium silicates such as forsterite are formed. See FORSTERITE MARBLE.

demantoid. The transparent, green variety of andradite. Also called URALIAN EMERALD.

dendrite. A tree-like crystal formation. Metal crystals grow in the first instance by branches developing in certain directions from the nuclei. Secondary branches are later thrown out at periodic intervals by the primary ones and in this way a skeleton crystal, or *dendrite*, is formed. The interstices between the branches are finally filled with solid which in a pure metal is indistinguishable from the skeleton. In many alloys, however, the final structure consists of skeletons of one composition in a matrix of another.

dendritic markings. Tree-like markings, usually quite superficial, occurring on joint-faces and other fractures in rocks, frequently consisting of oxide of manganese or of iron. Less frequently the appearance is due to the inclusion of a mineral of dendritic habit in another mineral or rock; e.g. chlorite in silica as in ' moss agate.'

Derbyshire spar. Popular name for FLUORSPAR.

descloizite. An uncommon compound of lead, zinc, and vanadium, crystallising in the orthorhombic system; occurs in the oxide zone of lead-zinc deposits.

desmine. See STILBITE.

devitrification. Deferred crystallisation which, in the case of glassy igneous rocks, converts obsidian and pitchstone into dull cryptocrystalline rocks (usually termed *felsites*) consisting of minute grains of quartz and feldspar. Such devitrified glasses give evidence of their originally vitreous nature by traces of perlitic and spherulitic textures.

diallage. A schillerised monoclinic pyroxene, in composition comparable with augite; occurs typically in basic igneous rocks such as gabbro.

dialogite. A mineral closely related to rhodocrosite, the trigonal carbonate of manganese.

diamond. This is one of the crystalline forms of carbon; it crystallises in the cubic system, rarely in cubes, commonly in forms resembling an octahedron, and less commonly in the tetrahedron. Curved faces are characteristic. It is the hardest mineral (10 in Mohs' scale); hence valuable as an abrasive, for arming rock-boring tools, etc., and as a gemstone. Occurs in the blue ground in the Kimberley District, in river gravels above the Vaal, in shore sands in S.W. Africa, also in Brazil, the Congo, British Guiana, and elsewhere. See BLACK DIAMOND, BORT.

diaspore. A group of minerals comprising diasporite, goethite, and manganite. *Diasporite* is an aluminium hydroxide occurring as platy orthorhombic crystals in clays, notably in some of the bauxites.

diatomite or **diatom earth.** A siliceous deposit occurring as a whitish powder consisting essentially of the frustules of diatoms (unicellular algae). Also known as KIESELGUHR.

dichroism. The property possessed by some crystals (tourmaline, for example) of absorbing the ordinary and extra-ordinary ray to different extents; this has the effect of giving to the crystal different colours according to the direction of the incident light.

dichroite. See CORDIERITE.

dickite. A form of hydrated silicate of aluminium, of the same chemical composition as kaolinite, with which it is grouped, and from which it differs only in the details of atomic structure and in certain physical properties.

dievrite. See ILVAITE.

dimorphism. The occurrence of a chemical substance as two distinct minerals, e.g. carbon as diamond and graphite, calcium carbonate as calcite or aragonite, FeS_2 as iron-pyrites and marcasite, potash feldspar as orthoclase (monoclinic) and microcline (triclinic).

diopside. One of the monoclinic pyroxenes, ideally consisting of silicate of calcium and magnesium, $CaMgSi_2O_6$, but commonly containing a variable content of $FeSi_2O_6$ in addition, and then strictly known as *ferriferous diopside.*

dioptase. A rare hydrated silicate of copper, crystallising in the trigonal system and found occasionally, as rich emerald-green crystals, in association with other copper ores. When first found

it was used as a gemstone. Called also EMERALD COPPER.

diorite. A coarse-grained deep-seated (plutonic) igneous rock of intermediate composition, consisting essentially of plagioclase feldspar (typically near andesine in composition) and hornblende, with or without biotite in addition. Differs from granodiorite in the absence of quartz. See also TONALITE.

dipyre, dipyrite. See MIZZONITE.

disthene. A less commonly used name for the mineral KYANITE. The name is applied on account of the striking differences in hardness, even on the same crystal face, when tested in different directions.

dodecahedron, rhombic. A crystal form of the cubic system, consisting of twelve exactly similar faces, each of which is a regular rhombus. Does not occur in the orthorhombic system, in spite of its name.

dog-tooth spar. A form of calcite in which the scalenohedron is dominant, giving a sharply pointed crystal like a canine tooth.

dolerite. The general name for basic igneous rocks of medium grain-size, occurring as minor intrusions or in the central parts of thick lava flows; much quarried for road metal. Typical dolerite consists of plagioclase near labradorite in composition, pyroxene, usually augite, and iron ore, usually ilmenite, together with their alteration products. See note at ALKALI-GRANITE, also MINVERITE, TESCHENITE.

dolomite. The double carbonate of calcium and magnesium, crystallising in the rhombohedral class of the trigonal system, occurring as cream-coloured crystals or masses with a distinctive pearly lustre, hence the synonym PEARL SPAR.

dolomite rock. A limestone consisting entirely of the mineral dolomite and therefore containing the $CaCO_3$ and $MgCO_3$ in equal molecular proportions. See also DOLOMITIC LIMESTONE.

dolomitic limestone. A calcareous sedimentary rock containing calcite or aragonite in addition to dolomite.

dome. A crystal form consisting of two similar inclined faces meeting in a horizontal edge, thus resembling the roof of a house. The term is frequently incorrectly applied to a four-faced form which is really a prism lying on an edge.

dravite. According to Kunitz, one of the three chief varieties of tourmaline; a complex borosilicate of magnesium and sodium; may be referred to as magnesium-tourmaline; used as a gemstone.

drusy cavities. GEODES.

drusy structure. See MIAROLITIC STRUCTURE.

dry bone ore. See SMITHSONITE.

dunite. A coarse-grained, deep-seated igneous rock, almost monomineralic, consisting essentially of olivine only, though chromite is an almost constant accessory. In several parts of the world (e.g. Bushveld Complex, S. Africa) it contains native platinum and related metals. Named from Mt. Dun, New Zealand.

durain. A constituent of dull coal; of firm, rather granular structure, sometimes containing many spores.

dysanalyte. A rare accessory mineral, apparently cubic, and related to perovskite in composition, but containing columbate as well as titanate of calcium, and a variable content of iron.

E

earth-wax. OZOKERITE.

earthy cobalt. A variety of WAD containing up to about 32% of cobalt oxide. Called also ASBOLITE.

eclogite. A coarse-grained deep-seated ultramafic rock, consisting essentially of pink garnet, green pyroxene (some of which is often chrome-diopside) and (rarely) kyanite. Good examples occur in the Fichtelgebirge and in the kimberlite pipes in S. Africa.

elaterite or **elastic bitumen.** A solid bitumen resembling dark-brown rubber; used in building. Sometimes known as MINERAL CAOUTCHOUC; occurs at Castleton, Derbyshire, and in Colorado and Utah.

electric calamine. See CALAMINE.

embolite. The chief silver ore in some of the Chile mines, occurring as yellow-green incrustations and masses. Chemically, chloride and bromide of silver.

emerald. The brilliant green gemstone, a form of BERYL; silicate of beryllium and aluminium, crystallising in hexagonal prismatic forms, occurring chiefly in mica-schists, and rarely in pegmatites. See BRAZILIAN— ORIENTAL— URALIAN—

emerald copper. See DIOPTASE.

emerald nickel. See ZARATITE.

emery. A finely granular intimate admixture of corundum and either magnetite or haematite, occurring naturally in Greece and localities in Asia Minor, etc.; used extensively as an abrasive.

emplectite. Sulphide of copper and bismuth, occurring at Tannenbaum and elsewhere as thin striated grey metallic prisms intimately associated with quartz.

enargite. Sulpharsenate of copper, often containing a little antimony. Occurs as black, metallic orthorhombic crystals in several mines in both N. and S. America.

en cabochon. A style of cutting used in the case of certain gemstones, notably garnets (carbuncles), and those gems which depend for their beauty largely upon minute orientated inclusions, such as cat's eye, crocidolite, star ruby, and star sapphire. Such stones are not faceted, but a smooth-domed surface is produced, the plan of the stone being circular or oval.

endellionite. Another name for BOURNONITE.

enstatite. An orthorhombic pyroxene, chemically a silicate of magnesium, $MgSiO_3$; it occurs as a rock-forming mineral, and also as an important constituent of other pyroxenes of more complex chemical composition. If the amount of associated iron is small, enstatite may occur as transparent green crystals, suitable for gems.

epidiorite. A term for altered gabbroic and doleritic rocks in which the original pyroxene has been replaced by fibrous amphibole. Other mineral changes have also taken place, and the rock may be regarded as a first step in the conversion, by dynamothermal metamorphism, of a basic igneous rock into a green schist.

epidote. This is a rare accessory but common secondary mineral in igneous rocks with a wide range of composition. Crystallises in the monoclinic system, in lustrous green-black to yellowish-green crystals. In composition closely related to clino-zoisite but contains iron, thus being hydrated silicate of calcium, aluminium, and iron. Also called PISTACITE.

epidotisation. A process of alteration, especially of igneous rocks in which the feldspar is albitised, with the separation of epidote and zoisite, representing the anorthite molecule of the original plagioclase. Pressure seems to be the dominant factor in this change.

epigenetic. See SYNGENETIC.

epistilbite. A colourless zeolite, chemically similar to heulandite; hydrated silicate of calcium and aluminium, crystallising in the monoclinic system.

epsomite or **Epsom salts.** Hydrated magnesium sulphate, $MgSO_4.7H_2O$; occurring in colourless orthorhombic prismatic crystals, botryoidal masses, or incrustations in gypsum mines and limestone caverns; common in solution in mineral waters. The chief source for commercial Epsom salts are the salt beds of Stassfurt.

erubescite. See BORNITE.

erythrite. Monoclinic hydrated arsenate of cobalt, occurring as reddish crystals or incrustations. Also called COBALT BLOOM.

essonite. A variety of HESSONITE.

euclase. A monoclinic member of the datolite group of minerals, occurring as prismatic, usually colourless, crystals. Chemically it is hydrated silicate of beryllium and aluminium.

eucrite. A coarse-grained, usually ophitic, deep-seated basic igneous rock, containing plagioclase near bytownite in composition, both ortho- and clino-pyroxenes, together with olivine. Eucrite is an important rock type in the Tertiary complexes of Scotland.

euhedral crystals. See IDIOMORPHIC CRYSTALS.

eutectic. Relating to a mixture of two or more substances having a minimum melting-point. Such a mixture behaves in some respects like a pure compound.

eutectic change. The transformation from the liquid to the solid state in a eutectic alloy. It involves the simultaneous crystallisation of two constituents in a binary system and of three in a ternary system.

euxenite. An uncommon mineral containing rare elements; a niobate and titanate of yttrium, erbium, cerium, and uranium, and valuable on this account. Commonly massive and brownish-black in colour; rarely, crystalline (orthorhombic prismatic forms).

extrusive rocks. Rocks formed by the consolidation of magma on the surface of the ground, as distinct from *intrusive rocks* which consolidate below ground. Commonly referred to as lava flows; normally of fine grain or even glassy.

F

facellite. See KALIOPHILITE.

facets. The flat sides of a crystal. The flat surfaces of varying shapes and sizes cut on precious stones.

fahlerz, fahlore. The grey-copper ore TETRAHEDRITE.

false amethyst, etc. In naming gemstones those engaged in the trade are guided by the colour of the gem rather than by its composition and physical characters. Thus, to them, all mauve stones are amethyst. Yet many minerals, when quite pure, are without colour; the addition of a minute amount of impurity of the right composition will impart to any of them a mauve tint. Unless the mauve stone is pure silica, it is incorrect to call it *amethyst*. For example, some specimens of corundum are mauve; these are known in the trade as ORIENTAL AMETHYST—one type of *false amethyst*.

false diamond. Several natural minerals are sometimes completely colourless and, when cut and polished, make brilliant gems. These include zircon, white sapphire, and white topaz. All three, however, are birefringent and can be easily distinguished from true diamond.

false lead. BLENDE (ZINC BLENDE).

false ruby. Some species of garnet (*Cape ruby*) and some species of spinel (*balas ruby, ruby spinel*) possess the colour of the ruby.

false topaz. A trade name applied to yellow quartz. See CITRINE.

famatinite. An orthorhombic sulphide of copper and antimony, Cu_3SbS_4, occurring in the Famatina Mts. (Argentina) and in Peru.

fayalite. A silicate of iron, Fe_2SiO_4, crystallising in the orthorhombic system, discovered originally at Fayal in the Azores, probably in a slag carried to the island as ballast; but found subsequently in igneous rocks, including pitchstone, obsidian, quartz-porphyry, and rhyolite. Also called IRON-OLIVINE.

feather ore. A plumose or acicular form of the orthorhombic sulphide of lead and antimony, occurring in the Harz Mts. and elsewhere. Also called JAMESONITE.

feldspar. A most important group of rock-forming silicates of aluminium, together with sodium, potassium, calcium, or barium, crystallising in closely similar forms in the monoclinic and triclinic systems. The chief members are *orthoclase* and *microcline* (potash feldspar); *albite* and *barbierite* (soda feldspar); and the *plagioclases* (soda-lime feldspar). The spelling *felspar* is due to a false derivation from German *fels* (rock); actually it is from Swedish *feldt* (field).

feldspathoids. A group of rock-forming minerals chemically related to the feldspars, but undersaturated with regard to silica content, and therefore incapable of free existence in the presence of magmatic silica. The chief members of the group are HAÜYNITE, LEUCITE, NEPHELINE, NOSEAN, and SODALITE.

felsite. An 'omnibus term' for fine-grained igneous rocks of acid composition, occurring as lavas or minor intrusions, and characterised by the felsitic texture— a fine patchy mosaic of quartz and feldspar, resulting from the devitrification of an originally glassy matrix.

felspar. See FELDSPAR.

felstone. An obsolete term for FELSITE.

ferberite. A member of the wolframite group of minerals; theoretically pure tungstate of iron, but usually some of the iron is replaced by manganese.

fergusonite. A rare mineral occurring in pegmatites; it consists of columbate and tantalate of yttrium, which may be partially replaced by iron, cerium, calcium, etc.

ferrimolybdite. See MOLYBDITE.

fibrolite. One of three crystalline forms of aluminium silicate, Al_2SiO_5, the others being andalusite (low temperature) and kyanite (high pressure). The silicate occurs commonly as felted aggregates of exceedingly thin fibrous crystals (hence the name *fibrolite*) in contact-metamorphosed aluminous sediments such as mudstones, shales, etc. Crystals of a pale sapphire blue are used as gems. Also called SILLIMANITE.

fibrous structure. If the crystals in a mineral aggregate are greatly elongated and of very slender cross-section, the structure is fibrous. (*a*) The fibres may be parallel, as in crocidolite and sometimes in gypsum and cerussite; when the fibres are very fine, there may be a silky lustre, as in crocidolite and satin-spar gypsum. (*b*) There is also a felt-like type. (*c*) Crystals may radiate from a centre, producing star-like groups, either coarse or fine, as frequently in pyrolusite, wavellite, natrolite and tourmaline, and sometimes in stibnite and other minerals.

fireclay. Clay consisting of minerals containing predominantly SiO_2 and Al_2O_3, with small proportions of Fe_2O_3, CaO, MgO, etc. Those clays which soften only at high temperatures are used widely as refractories in metallurgical and other furnaces. Fireclays occur abundantly in the Carboniferous System, as 'seat earths' underneath the coal-seams.

fire opal. A variety of opal (amorphous silica) characterised by a brilliant orange-flame colour. Particularly good specimens, prized as gemstones, are of Mexican or Australian origin.

flèches d'amour. Acicular, hair-like crystals of rutile, a crystalline form of oxide of titanium, TiO_2, embedded in quartz. Used as a semi-precious gem-stone. Also called LOVE ARROWS—the literal translation of *flèches d'amour*.

flint. Flints are concretions of silica, sometimes tabular, but usually irregular in form, distributed in countless numbers on the bedding planes of the Upper Chalk. Thought to have been formed by the segregation of organic silica derived from siliceous sponges. See also PARAMUDRAS.

float-stone. A coarse, porous, friable variety of impure silica, consisting chiefly of the siliceous skeletons of infusoria. On account of its porosity it floats on water until saturated, hence the name.

flos ferri. This is a massive form (as distinct from individual crystals) of the orthorhombic carbonate of calcium, *aragonite*, some of the masses resembling delicate coralline growths; deposited from hot springs.

fluor, also called FLUOR-SPAR. Name derived from the use of the spar as a flux.

fluorescence. The absorption of radiation of a particular wavelength by a substance and its re-emission as light of greater wavelength. With many substances, such as quinine sulphate and fluor-spar (the origin of the word), ultra-violet radiation produces visible fluorescence.

fluor-spar. This is native calcium fluoride, CaF_2, crystallising in the cubic system, commonly in simple cubes. Occasionally colourless, yellow, green, but typically purple; the coloured varieties fluoresce strongly in ultra-violet light. Also called FLUORITE.

foliation. The arrangement of minerals normally possessing a platy habit (such as the micas, chlorites, and talc) in folia or leaves, lying with their principal faces and cleavages in parallel planes; due to development under great pressure during regional metamorphism.

forsterite. An end-member of the olivine group of minerals, crystallising in the orthorhombic system. Chemically, forsterite is silicate of magnesium, Mg_2SiO_4.

forsterite-marble. A characteristic product of the contact-metamorphism of magnesian (dolomitic) limestones containing silica of organic or inorganic origin. The dolomite splits up into magnesia, CO_2 and $CaCO_3$. The first combines with the silica to form forsterite, while the calcium

carbonate recrystallises as marble. Also called OPHICALCITE.

fossil. A relic of some former living thing —plant or animal—embedded in, or dug out of, the superficial deposits of past geological periods.

fossil resin. See AMBER, SUCCINITE, KAURI GUM, COPALS.

fossil wood. See LIGNITE, JET, BOG OAK.

fractional crystallisation. The formation, at successively lower temperatures, of the component minerals in a magma, coupled with the tendency for the components which crystallise at high temperatures to separate, on account of their high specific gravity, thus giving a concentration in the lower parts of a magma body.

fracture. The broken surface of a mineral as distinct from its cleavage. The fracture is described, in different cases, as conchoidal (shell-like), platy or flat, smooth, hackly (like that of cast-iron), or earthy. Thus calcite has a perfect rhombohedral cleavage (i.e. it splits readily parallel to the six faces of the rhombohedron), but has a conchoidal fracture.

frangibility. Tendency to break; capacity of being broken. To be distinguished from hardness; diamond is quite brittle.

franklinite. Zinc-manganese spinel, occurring rarely as at the type-locality, Franklin Furnace, New Jersey.

French chalk. The mineral talc ground into a state of fine subdivision, its softness and its perfect cleavage contributing to its special properties when used as a dry lubricant.

fuchsite. A bright green variant of MUSCOVITE in which chromium replaces some of the aluminium.

fulgurites. Tubular bodies produced by lightning in loose unconsolidated sand; caused by the vitrification of the sand grains, forming quartz glass. Although of very narrow cross-section, some specimens have been found to exceed 20 ft. in length. Also called LIGHTNING TUBES.

fuller's earth. A non-plastic clay consisting essentially of the mineral montmorillonite, and similar in this respect to bentonite. Used originally in 'fulling,' i.e. absorbing fats from wool, hence the name.

fusain. 'Mineral charcoal,' one of the important constituents of coal, which in household coal alternates with durain, etc., and gives rise to the characteristic stratification. Fusain consists of plant remains from which the volatiles have been eliminated.

G

gabbro. The name of a rock clan, and also of a specific igneous rock type. The rock gabbro is a coarse-grained plutonite, consisting essentially of plagioclase, near labradorite in composition, and clinopyroxene, with or without olivine in addition. The gabbro clan includes also norite, eucrite, troctolite, kentallenite, etc., together with their medium- and fine-grained equivalents.

gahnite. A mineral belonging to the spinel group; occurs as grey octahedral cubic crystals. Also known as ZINC-SPINEL (see SPINEL), the composition being zinc aluminate, $ZnO \cdot Al_2O_3$.

galactite. A mineral of the zeolite group, intermediate in composition between natrolite and mesolite.

galena or **lead glance.** Sulphide of lead, PbS; the commonest ore of lead, occurring as grey cubic crystals, often associated with zinc-blende, in mineralised veins. Silver sulphide, argentite, which is isomorphous with galena, may be present. See also SILVER LEAD ORE.

ganister. A particularly pure and even-grained siliceous grit or loosely cemented quartzite, occurring in the Upper Carboniferous of the Midlands; highly prized in the manufacture of silica-bricks. Also GANNISTER.

garnet. Name for a group of minerals which crystallise in the cubic system. Some species occur rarely in igneous rocks, but are characteristic of metamorphic rocks, such as garnet-micaschist, garnet gneiss, and eclogite. Some species are of value as gems, rivalling ruby. See ANDRADITE, GROSSULARITE, MELANITE, PYROPE, SPESSARTITE.

garnierite. A bright-green nickeliferous silicate of magnesium, a decomposition product of olivine. In external form garnierite resembles chalcedony, and differs from chrysolite chiefly in this respect.

gaylussite. A rare grey hydrated carbonate of sodium and calcium, occurring in lacustrine deposits.

gehlenite. A tetragonal silicate of calcium and aluminium; an end-member of an isomorphous series collectively known as melilite.

geodes. Large cavities in rocks, lined with crystals that were free to grow inwards.

geology. The science which investigates the history of the earth's crust, from the earliest times to the commencement of the Historical Period. It deals with the compositions, arrangement, and origins of the rocks of the earth's crust, and with the processes involved in the evolution of its present structure. Geology is now divided into several branches: *physical geology*, the study of the processes of sedimentation and denudation, the work of the atmosphere, water, ice, rivers, and the sea, the study of rock structures; *petrology*, the study of the nature, composition, textures, and origins of igneous, metamorphic, and sedimentary rocks and of the metallic ores; *mineralogy*, the study of the compositions, physical characters (including crystal form) of the natural minerals; *stratigraphy* or *historical geology*; and *palaeontology* (with *palaeo-*

botany), which traces the history of life on this planet and the structures of, and relationships between, the several kinds of organisms.

German lapiz. See SWISS LAPIZ.

gersdorffite. Metallic grey sulphide-arsenide of nickel, occurring as cubic crystals or in granular or massive forms.

geyserite. See SILICEOUS SINTER.

ghost crystal. A crystal within which may be seen an early stage of growth, outlined by a thin deposit of dust or other mineral deposit.

gibbsite. Hydrated oxide of aluminium, $Al_2O_3 \cdot 3H_2O$, occurring as minute mica-like crystals, concretional masses, or incrustations. An important constituent of bauxite. Also called HYDRARGILLITE.

gilsonite. See UINTAITE.

girasol. A variety of fire opal of a bright hyacinth-red colour; the finest specimens show a faint bluish opalescence emanating from the centre of the stone.

glance. A lustrous metallic sulphide; from German *glanz*, brightness, lustre.

glass. A hard, amorphous, brittle substance, made by fusing together one or more of the oxides of silicon, boron, or phosphorus, with certain basic oxides (e.g. sodium, magnesium, calcium, potassium), and cooling the product rapidly to prevent crystallisation or devitrification. See also NATURAL GLASS.

glassy feldspar. Two varieties of potash feldspar occur as transparent colourless crystals—SANIDINE and ADULARIA. Transparent yellow orthoclase also occurs but is very rare.

Glauber salt. Properly termed MIRABILITE (hydrated sodium sulphate, $Na_2SO_4 \cdot 10H_2O$). A monoclinic mineral formed in salt lakes, deposited by hot springs, or resulting from the action of volcanic gases on sea water. Obtained from Austria and the Great Salt Lake (Utah).

glauberite. Monoclinic sulphate of sodium and calcium, occurring with rock salt, anhydrite, etc., in saline deposits.

glaucodote. A tin-white orthorhombic sulph-arsenide of iron and cobalt, occurring with cobaltite in Huasco Province, Chile. Also spelt GLAUCODOT.

glauconite. Hydrated silicate of potassium and iron, a green mineral that forms on submerged banks, such as the Agulhas Bank. Its occurrence in sands and sandstones is regarded, therefore, as a certain indication of accumulation under marine conditions.

glaucophane. A rare monoclinic amphibole, essentially metasilicate of sodium, magnesium, and aluminium, occurring in schists resulting from the regional metamorphism of soda-rich igneous rocks, such as spilites in Anglesey and elsewhere.

globulites. Crystallites (i.e. incipient crystals) of minute size and spherical shape occurring in natural glasses such as pitchstones.

gneiss. A metamorphic rock of coarse

grain-size, characterised by a mineral banding, in which the light minerals (quartz and feldspar) are separated from the dark ones (mica and/or hornblende). The layers of dark minerals are foliated, while the light bands are granulitic. See also METAMORPHISM.

goethite. Orthorhombic hydrated oxide of iron with composition $Fe_2O_3 \cdot H_2O$. Externally resembles limonite, with which it is frequently misidentified. See IRON ORES, LIMONITE.

gold. A heavy, soft, yellow, metallic element in the first group of the periodic system. Symbol, Au. At. no. 79, at. wt. 197·2, sp. gr. at 20° C. 19·3, m.p. 1063° C.

gold amalgam. A variety of native gold containing approximately 60% of mercury; discovered in Colombia and occurs also in the Mariposa district of California.

golden beryl. A clear yellow variety of BERYL, prized as a gemstone. *Heliodor* is a variety from S.W. Africa.

gooseberry stone. The literal translation of the Latinised form GROSSULARITE, so called from the occurrence of this green garnet in rounded crystals somewhat vaguely resembling gooseberries in form and colour.

goslarite. Zinc sulphate, a rare mineral precipitated from water seeping through the walls of lead-mines; formed by the oxidation of sphalerite.

gouttes d'eau. Literally 'drops of water'; PINGOS D'AGOA; an old term applied to the whitest of the Brazilian topaz crystals, which when cut and polished rival diamond in brilliancy, but lack the fire of the latter gem.

granite. A coarse-grained igneous rock containing megascopic quartz, averaging 25%, much feldspar (orthoclase, microcline, sodic plagioclase), and mica or other coloured minerals. In the wide sense granite includes alkali-granites, adamellites, and granodiorites, while the *granite clan* includes the medium- and fine-grained equivalents of these rock types. Because of its extreme hardness, granite is used largely for heavy engineering and building works and for road metalling.

granitoid texture. A rock fabric in which the minerals do not possess crystal outlines but occur in shapeless interlocking grains. Such rocks are in the coarse grain-size group. Also called XENOMORPHIC GRANULAR TEXTURE.

granular structure. Exhibited by a mineral showing crystalline grains, but not external crystal faces; e.g. marble.

graphic tellurium. An obsolete name applied in 1814 to the mineral SYLVANITE. The crystals are frequently twinned in such a fashion as to resemble runic characters. See GRAPHIC TEXTURE.

graphic texture. A rock texture in which one mineral intimately intergrown with another occurs in a form simulating ancient writing, especially runic characters.

graphite. This is one of the two naturally occurring forms of crystalline carbon, the other being diamond. Sp. gr. 2·23; graphite contains also up to 5% of silica. It occurs as black, soft masses and, rarely, as crystals (of flaky structure and apparently hexagonal) in igneous rocks; in larger quantities in schists, particularly in metamorphosed carbonaceous clays and shales; also in contact-metamorphosed coals and in meteorites. A well-known British locality is Borrowdale in Cumberland, where the amount available was sufficient for exploitation in the manufacture of black lead. Also called BLACK LEAD, PLUMBAGO.

gravel. The name of the aggregate consisting dominantly of pebbles, though usually a considerable amount of sand is intercalated.

greasy feel. Some minerals are greasy or soapy to the touch; e.g. talc, sometimes called soapstone.

green carbonate of copper. See MALACHITE.

green lead ore. An obsolete name for PYROMORPHITE.

green vitriol. Popular name for MELANTERITE.

Greenland spar. See CRYOLITE.

greenockite. Crystalline cadmium sulphide, occurring, as small yellow hexagonal crystals exhibiting polar symmetry, in cavities in altered lavas at Bishopton, Renfrewshire, Scotland.

greisen. A pneumatolytic derivative of granite, in which feldspar has been suppressed and white mica produced in its place. A constant accessory is topaz, while fluorite is usually present. Common in some of the Cornish granites. See also PNEUMATOLYSIS.

grey copper ore. See TETRAHEDRITE.

grit. Siliceous sediment, loose or indurated, the component grains being angular. Contrast *sand* and *sandstone*, in which the grains are rounded.

grossularite or **grossular.** A green garnet, the composition being represented by $3CaO \cdot Al_2O_3 \cdot 3SiO_2$; formed in the contact-metamorphism of impure limestone. (A massive green variety is known as *Transvaal jade*.) Also called GOOSEBERRY STONE.

gypsum. Name given to crystalline hydrated sulphate of calcium, $CaSO_4 \cdot 2H_2O$. Occurs massive as alabaster, fibrous as satin spar, and as clear, colourless monoclinic crystals known as selenite. Used in the manufacture of plaster of Paris.

H

habit. A term used to cover the varying development of the crystal forms possessed by any one mineral. Thus calcite may occur as crystals showing the faces of the hexagonal prism, basal pinacoid, scalenohedron, and rhombohedron. According to the relative development or *dominance* of one or other of these forms, the habit may be prismatic, tabular, scalenohedral, or rhombohedral.

hackly fracture. When a mineral, e.g. native copper, presents sharp points, the fracture is said to be hackly. Cast iron also has this peculiarity.

haematite. An important oxide of iron, Fe_2O_3, crystallising in the trigonal system. It occurs in a number of different forms : kidney iron-ore massive, as found in the iron mines in Lancashire and Cumberland ; specular iron-ore in groups of beautiful, lustrous, rhombohedral crystals as, for example, from Elba ; bedded ores of sedimentary origin, as in the Carboniferous Limestone of S. Wales ; and as a cement and pigment in sandstones. The Clinton ore is the most important oölitic haematite in the U.S.A. (see CLINTON LIMESTONES). The Wabana ore in Newfoundland is also haematitic in part, but most of the iron produced in N. America comes from the ' iron ranges ' of the Lake Superior district, especially the Mesabi Range, Minn.

hair-copper. See CHALCOTRICHITE.

halite. A name for common or rock salt, the naturally occurring form of sodium chloride, crystallising in the cubic system ; represented in the Purbeck Series by clay pseudomorphs, and forming deposits of considerable thickness in close association with anhydrite and gypsum in the Permian and Triassic rocks of this and other countries. Deposits of commercial value occur in Cheshire, Lancashire, Co. Antrim, and Somerset, the salt being pumped out as brine from the Keuper Marl ; the Stassfurt deposits in Germany and those of Wieliczka in Poland are famous. In the U.S.A. valuable salt deposits occur in the Salina beds of Silurian age, worked in Michigan, New York, Ohio, etc. ; also in the overlying Mississippian. Salt of Permian age is important in Kansas and Oklahoma. Salt domes occur in Louisiana and Texas.

halloysite. One of the so-called clay minerals, apparently amorphous ; consists of hydrated aluminium silicate.

halotrichite. Hydrated sulphate of iron and aluminium, occurring rarely as yellowish fibrous colourless crystals in rocks that have been affected by the action of sulphuric acid around fumaroles. Also called IRON ALUM.

hardness. The resistance which a mineral offers to abrasion. The absolute hardness is measured with the aid of a sclerometer. The comparative hardness is expressed in terms of Mohs' scale, and is determined by testing against ten standard minerals: (1) talc, (2) gypsum, (3) calcite, (4) fluorite, (5) apatite, (6) orthoclase, (7) quartz, (8) topaz, (9) corundum, (10) diamond. Thus a mineral with ' hardness 5 ' will scratch or abrade fluorite, but will be scratched by orthoclase. Hardness varies on different faces of a crystal, and in some cases (e.g. kyanite) in different directions on any one face.

harmotome. A member of the zeolite group, hydrated silicate of aluminium and barium, crystallising in the monoclinic system, though the symmetry approaches that of the tetragonal system. Best known by reason of the distinctive cruciform twin groups that are not uncommon.

hauerite. A rare brownish-black sulphide of manganese, occurring as small cubic crystals in clay or schist.

hausmannite. A blackish-brown crystalline form of manganese oxide, occurring (rarely) with other manganese ores, as in the Lake Superior district.

haüynite or **haüyne.** A feldspathoid, crystallising in the cubic system, consisting essentially of silicate of aluminium and sodium, with sodium sulphate ; occurs as small blue crystals, chiefly in soda-trachytes.

hawk's eye. A dark blue form of silicified crocidolite found in Griqualand West.

heavy spar. See BARYTES.

hedenbergite. An important lime-iron pyroxene, $CaFeSi_2O_6$, occurring as black crystals, and also as a component in many of the rock-forming clinopyroxenes.

heliodor. A beautiful variety of clear yellow beryl occurring near Rössing in S.W. Africa ; much prized as a gemstone.

heliotrope. See BLOODSTONE.

hemicrystalline rocks. Those rocks of igneous origin which contain some interstitial glass, in addition to crystalline minerals. Cf. HOLOCRYSTALLINE ROCKS.

hemimorphism. The development of polar symmetry in minerals, in consequence of which different forms are exhibited at the ends of bi-terminated crystals. Hemimorphite shows this character in a marked degree.

hemimorphite. An orthorhombic hydrous silicate of zinc ; one of the best minerals for demonstrating polar symmetry, the two ends being distinctly dissimilar. In U.S.A. called CALAMINE or ELECTRIC CALAMINE.

hercynite. See under SPINEL.

herzenbergite. A rare decomposition product of tin ores, having the composition, tin sulphide, SnS ; described originally from a locality in Bolivia.

hessite. Telluride of silver, a metallic grey cubic mineral occurring in silver ores in various parts of the world, notably at Savodinski in the Altai Mts. in Siberia.

hessonite. Name for a variety of GARNET containing a preponderance of the grossularite molecule, and characterised by a pleasing reddish-brown colour. Also called CINNAMON STONE.

hetaerolite or **heterolite.** A very rare double oxide of zinc and manganese, occurring in ore deposits as black tetragonal and fibrous crystals.

heulandite. One of the best-known zeolites, beautifully crystalline, occurring as coffin-shaped monoclinic crystals in cavities in decomposed basic igneous rocks. In composition similar to plagioclase, but with a high content of water.

hewettite. A very rare hydroxide of vanadium and calcium, occurring as slender orthorhombic crystals in the vanadium deposits of Peru.

hexagonal system. A crystal system in which three equal coplanar axes intersect at an angle of 60°, and a fourth, perpendicular to the others, is of a different length.

hiddenite. See SPODUMENE.

holocrystalline rocks. Those igneous rocks in which all the components are crystalline; glass is absent. Cf. HEMICRYSTALLINE ROCKS.

hopeite. Hydrous phosphate of zinc, occurring very rarely in zinc mines as orthorhombic grey crystals.

hornblende. An amphibole, a common rock-forming mineral of complex composition, essentially silicate of calcium, magnesium, and iron, with smaller amounts of potash, soda, and hydroxyl; crystallises in the monoclinic system; occurs as black crystals or grains in many different types of igneous and metamorphic rocks, including hornblende-granite, syenite, diorite, andesite, etc., and hornblende-schist and amphibolite.

hornblende-gneiss. A coarse-grained metamorphic rock, containing hornblende as the dominant coloured constituent, together with feldspar and quartz, the texture being that typical of the gneisses. Differs from hornblende-schist in grain-size and texture only.

hornblende-granite. A type of granite, usually adamellite or granodiorite, containing hornblende as an essential constituent; with decreasing quartz, grades through tonalite into normal diorite.

hornblende-schist. A type of green schist, formed from basic igneous rocks by regional metamorphism, and consisting essentially of sodic plagioclase, hornblende, and sphene, frequently with magnetite and epidote. See also GLAUCOPHANE.

horn lead. The translation of the French term *plomb corné*, sometimes applied to the mineral PHOSGENITE.

hornsilver. See CERARGYRITE.

hornstone. This is an old name for rocks differing widely in composition and origin, characterised by their flinty, compact appearance. The term *hornfels* is still used for fine-textured contact-altered argillaceous rocks.

horse-flesh ore. A name applied by Cornish miners to the mineral BORNITE on account of its reddish-brown colour.

hübnerite or **huebnerite.** Tungstate of manganese, one of the end members of a variable series (the other being *ferberite*, tungstate of iron), commonly known as wolfram or wolframite. A product of pneumatolysis; associated with such minerals as scheelite, cassiterite, etc.

hullite. CHLOROPHAEITE.

Hungarian cat's-eye. An inferior greenish cat's-eye obtained in the Fichtelgebirge in Bavaria. No such stone occurs in Hungary.

hyacinth. See JACINTH.

hyalite. A colourless transparent variety of OPAL, occurring as globular concretions and crusts. Also called MÜLLER'S GLASS.

hyalophane. One of the rarer feldspars, consisting of the components of orthoclase and celsian (baryta-feldspar) in combination, and intermediate in composition between these two minerals. It occurs in colourless crystals in dolomite in manganese mines in Sweden, apparently as a contact mineral.

hydrargillite. See GIBBSITE.

hydrocalumite. A mnemonic name applied by C. E. Tilley to a new mineral occurring in the metamorphic aureole of the dolerite at Scawt Hill, Antrim; it consists of hydrated calcium aluminate, and has the composition of $4CaO \cdot Al_2O_3 \cdot 12H_2O$.

hydrocerussite. A rare colourless anhydrous basic carbonate of lead occurring as an encrustation on native lead or on galena.

hydrohaematite. $Fe_2O_3 \cdot nH_2O$. Probably a mixture of the two minerals *haematite* and *goethite*, the former being in excess. It is fibrous and red in the mass, with an orange tint when powdered. Also called TURGITE.

hydromagnesite. Magnesium hydroxide and carbonate, occurring as whitish amorphous masses, or rarely as monoclinic crystals in serpentines. An alteration product of the magnesium silicate minerals in the ultramafic rocks.

hydrophane. A variety of cacholong opal which, when dry, is almost opaque, with a pearly lustre, but becomes transparent when soaked with water, as implied in the name.

hydrozincite. A monoclinic hydroxide and carbonate of zinc, in some specimens partly replaced by copper. It is an uncommon ore, occurring with smithsonite in the oxide zone of some lodes. Also called ZINC BLOOM.

hypersthene. This is an important rock-forming silicate of magnesium and iron, $(Mg,Fe)SiO_3$, crystallising in the orthorhombic system; an essential constituent of norite, hypersthene-pyroxenite, hypersthenite, hypersthene-andesite, and charnockite.

hypidiomorphic or **subhedral.** A term referring to the texture of igneous rocks in which some of the component minerals show crystal contours, the others occurring in irregular grains. Cf. IDIOMORPHIC.

hypocrystalline. See HEMICRYSTALLINE.

4

I

Iceland agate. A name quite erroneously applied to the natural glass OBSIDIAN.

Iceland spar. A very pure transparent and crystalline form of calcium carbonate, first brought from Iceland. It has perfect cleavage and is noted for its double refraction.

idiomorphic (euhedral) crystals. Rock minerals which are bounded by the crystal faces peculiar to the species. Cf. ALLOTRIOMORPHIC (anhedral) and HYPIDIOMORPHIC (subhedral).

idocrase. A hydrated silicate of lime and alumina, crystallising in the tetragonal system. Also called VESUVIANITE.

ilmenite. An oxide of iron and titanium, crystallising in the trigonal system; a widespread accessory mineral in igneous rocks, especially in those of basic composition.

ilmenorutile. A black variety of titanium oxide, containing iron in the form of ferrous titanate, niobate, and tantalate; crystallises in the tetragonal system.

ilvaite. (Latin *Ilva*, Elba.) Silicate of iron and calcium, a little oxide of manganese frequently being present. It crystallises in the orthorhombic system. Also called DIEVRITE.

inclusion. A foreign body (gas, liquid, glass or mineral) enclosed by a mineral. See also XENOLITH.

Indian topaz. See CITRINE.

indianite. See ANORTHITE.

indicolite or indigolite. A blue (either pale or bluish-black) variety of tourmaline.

indigo copper. See COVELLITE.

intergranular texture. A texture characteristic of holocrystalline basalts and doleritic rocks, due to the aggregation of augite grains between feldspar laths arranged in a network.

intergrowths of crystals. Intergrowths are common: two crystals growing from near centres fill the space between and on meeting interfere; beginning independently, they are related in no definite way.

intermediate igneous rocks. Igneous rocks, containing from 55% to 66% of silica, and essentially intermediate in composition between the acid (granitic) and basic (gabbroic or basaltic) rocks:—e.g. SYENITE and DIORITE.

interpenetration twins. Two or more crystals united in a regular fashion, according to a fixed plan (the *twin law*), the individual crystals appearing to have grown through one another.

intrusions. Bodies of igneous rocks of varying size and structure which, in the condition of magma, were intruded into the pre-existing rocks of the earth's crust. Such rocks are referred to as *intrusive rocks*; cf. EXTRUSIVE ROCKS.

iolite. See CORDIERITE.

iridosmine. See OSMIRIDIUM.

iris. A form of quartz showing chromatic reflections of light from fractures, often produced artificially by suddenly cooling a heated crystal. Also called RAINBOW QUARTZ.

iron alum. See HALOTRICHITE.

iron carbonate. See CHALYBITE.

iron glance. From the German *Eisenglanz*, a name often applied to specular iron-ore (haematite).

iron meteorites. A popular name for those meteorites which consist essentially of nickel-iron, in the form of kamacite, taenite, plessite, etc.

iron, native. Native iron is very rare, as it oxidises; the nickel-iron of meteorites is more common.

iron niobate. See COLUMBITE.

iron-olivine. See FAYALITE.

iron ores. Rocks or deposits containing iron-rich compounds in workable amounts; they may be primary or secondary; they may occur as irregular masses, as lodes or veins, or interbedded with sedimentary strata. See CHALYBITE, CHAMOSITE, GOETHITE, HAEMATITE, LIMONITE, MAGNETITE.

iron oxides. See HAEMATITE, MAGNETITE.

iron pan. A hard layer often found in sands and gravels; caused by the precipitation of iron salts from percolating waters. It is formed a short distance below the soil surface.

iron phosphate. See VIVIANITE.

iron pyrite or pyrites. Known as 'fool's gold.' Sulphide of iron, crystallising in the cubic system. It is brassy-yellow in colour and of very common occurrence. Also called MUNDIC.

iron silicates. See AUGITE, BRONZITE, CROCIDOLITE, DIOPSIDE, HYPERSTHENE, etc.

ironstone. Carbonate of iron, clay, and carbonaceous matter, found in nodules, layers, or beds in the coal measures. See CHALYBITE.

iron sulphides. See CHALCOPYRITE, IRON PYRITES, MARCASITE, PYRRHOTITE.

iserine. Probably a ferruginous rutile, though formerly considered to be a variety of ilmenite. Found at Iserwiese (Bohemia).

isodimorphous. Existing in two isomorphous crystalline forms.

isomorphism. The name given to the phenomenon whereby two or more minerals, which are closely similar in their chemical constitution, crystallise in the same class of the same system of symmetry, and develop very similar forms.

Italian asbestos. A name often given to tremolite asbestos to distinguish it from Canadian or chrysotile asbestos. It is extensively quarried in Piedmont and Lombardy.

ixiolite. See TAPIOLITE.

J

jacinth or hyacinth. The aurora-red variety of transparent zircon, used as a gemstone. A cinnamon-coloured variety of grossularite from Ceylon is also called *hyacinth*.

jacobsite. An oxide of magnesium, iron, and manganese, which crystallises in the cubic system (usually in the form of distorted octahedra).

jade. A general term loosely used to include various mineral substances of tough texture and of a green colour. It properly embraces jadeite and nephrite, but green varieties of sillimanite, pectolite, serpentine, vesuvianite, and garnet are sometimes included.

jadeite. A metasilicate of sodium and aluminium which crystallises in the monoclinic system. It is green in colour and has long been prized in the Orient. The finest material comes from Mogaung, Upper Burma.

jamesonite. See FEATHER ORE.

jargons, jargoons. A name given in the gem trade to the zircons (chiefly of golden-yellow colour) from Ceylon. They resemble diamonds in lustre but are less valuable. See also JACINTH.

jarosite. A hydrated sulphate of iron and potassium crystallising in the trigonal system.

jasp-opal. See OPAL JASPER.

jasper. This is an impure opaque silica, commonly red owing to the presence of iron oxides in the silica.

jet. A hard coal-black variety of lignite, showing under the microscope the structure of coniferous wood.

Job's-tears. Rounded grains of chrysolite (olivine) found associated with garnet in certain localities.

K

kainite. Hydrous sulphate of magnesium, with potassium chloride, which crystallises in the monoclinic system. It usually occurs in the upper portions of salt deposits, e.g. at Stassfurt (Germany).

kalinite. Hydrous sulphate of potassium and aluminium, which probably crystallises in the monoclinic system. It has the same composition as potash alum. They both occur as an efflorescence upon argillaceous minerals, and in connexion with volcanoes.

kaliophilite. Silicate of potassium and aluminium, which crystallises in the hexagonal system. It commonly contains small amounts of nepheline. Also called PHACELLITE or FACELLITE.

kamacite. A variety of nickeliferous iron, found in meteorites.

kampylite, campylite. A variety of mimetite, composed of lead chloride and lead arsenate, crystallising, in the form of barrel-shaped crystals, in the hexagonal system.

kaolin. See CHINA CLAY.

kaolinisation. The processes whereby feldspars and other alumino-silicates are altered to kaolin, the active agents being,

apparently, magmatic water and carbon dioxide.

kaolinite. A finely crystalline form of hydrated aluminium silicate $(OH)_4Al_2Si_2O_5$, occurring as minute monoclinic flaky crystals with a perfect basal cleavage, resulting chiefly from the alteration of feldspars under conditions of hydrothermal or pneumatolytic metamorphism. The kaolin group of minerals includes also the recently recognised isomers *dickite* and *nacrite*.

kauri gum. A gum found in New Zealand, used for varnishes and linoleum cements. It is the resinous exudation of the *kauri pine (Agathis australis)*. See COPALS and cf. AMBER.

kermesite. Oxysulphide of antimony, which crystallises either in the orthorhombic or the monoclinic system. It is a secondary mineral occurring as the alteration product of stibnite. Also called PYROSTIBNITE.

kernite. Hydrated oxide of sodium and boron, crystallising in the monoclinic system. It is usually associated with ulexite and is a source of borates. Also called RASORITE.

kidney ore. A variety of the mineral haematite, the sesquioxide of iron, which occurs in reniform masses, hence the name.

kidney stone. A name given to NEPHRITE, which was once supposed to be efficacious in diseases of the kidney (Greek *nephros*, kidney).

kieselguhr. See DIATOMITE.

kieserite. Hydrous sulphate of magnesium which crystallises in the monoclinic system; found in large amounts in the salt deposits of Germany.

kimberlite. A type of mica-peridotite, occurring in volcanic pipes in South Africa, usually highly altered and containing xenoliths of many types of ultramafic rocks, and diamonds.

king's yellow. See ORPIMENT.

knitted structure. A structure found in serpentine, consisting of two sets of interlacing scales lying parallel to the original cleavage planes of a nonaluminous augite, from which it was derived.

krokidolite. See CROCIDOLITE.

kunzite. See SPODUMENE.

kyanite or **cyanite.** Name for a silicate of aluminium which crystallises in the triclinic system. It usually occurs as long-bladed crystals, blue in colour, in metamorphic rocks. See also DISTHENE.

L

labradorescence. A brilliant change of colour caused in some stones, e.g. labradorite, by the presence of minute enclosed crystalline plates, or aligned rod-like inclusions.

labradorite. A common plagioclase feldspar

containing approximately equal amounts of the albite and anorthite molecules; occurs in basic igneous rocks; characterised by a beautiful play of colours in some specimens, due to schiller structure. Named from Labrador, whence fine specimens were sent over to Europe by Moravian settlers. Also LABRADOR-SPAR.

lake-ore. Another name for BOG IRON-ORE. See also LIMONITE.

lamprophyres. Igneous rocks usually occurring as dykes; characterised by abnormally high contents of dark-coloured silicates, such as biotite, hornblende, and augite, and a correspondingly small amount of feldspar, some being feldspar-free.

lanarkite. A very rare monoclinic sulphate of lead, occurring with anglesite and leadhillite (into which it easily alters) at Leadhills, Lanarkshire, Scotland.

langite. A very rare ore of copper occurring in Cornwall, blue to green in colour; essentially hydrated copper sulphate, crystallising in the orthorhombic system.

lapis lazuli. This is the original sapphire of the ancients, a beautiful blue stone used extensively for ornamental purposes; it consists of calcite stained deep-blue by three cubic minerals, lazurite, sodalite, and haüyne.

larnite. Orthosilicate of calcium, Ca_2SiO_4, discovered in the contact zone of a Tertiary dolerite intrusive into chalk containing flint nodules; formed by reaction between the calcium carbonate of the former and the silica of the latter. Cf. WOLLASTONITE.

laterite. An aeolian clay formed under tropical climatic conditions by the weathering of igneous rocks, usually of basic composition. Consists chiefly of hydroxides of iron and aluminium, grading through increase of the latter into bauxite.

laumontite. A zeolite consisting essentially of hydrated silicate of calcium and aluminium, crystallising in the monoclinic system; occurs in cavities in igneous rocks and in veins in schists and slates.

laurionite. Oxychloride of lead, exceedingly rare, found in ancient lead slags at Laurium in Greece.

laurite. An iron-black sulphide of ruthenium and osmium occurring as small cubic crystals (octahedra), associated with platinum, in Borneo and Oregon.

lautarite. Monoclinic iodate of calcium, occurring rarely in caliche in Chile.

lazulite. A deep azure blue, strongly pleochroic mineral, crystallising in the monoclinic system. In composition essentially a hydrated phosphate of aluminium, magnesium, and iron, with a little calcium.

lazurite. An ultramarine-blue mineral occurring in cubic crystals or shapeless masses; it consists of silicate of sodium and aluminium with some sulphur. A constituent of LAPIS-LAZULI.

lead. Symbol, Pb. A metallic element in the fourth group of the periodic system. At. wt. 207·2, at. no. 82, valency 2 or 4, m.p. 327·5° C., sp. gr. at 20° C. 11·35. Specific electrical resistivity 20·65 microhms per c.c. The metal is bluish-grey, the heaviest and softest of the common metals. Lead occurs very rarely in the native form, and then appears to have been formed by fusion of some simple lead ore accidentally incorporated in lava.

lead arsenate. See MIMETITE.

lead carbonate. $PbCO_3$. Occurs in nature as CERUSSITE.

lead chromate. See CROCOITE.

lead glance. See GALENA.

leadhillite. Carbonate and sulphate of lead, so called from its occurrence, with other ores of lead, at Leadhills, Lanarkshire, Scotland. See LANARKITE.

lead molybdate. See WULFENITE.

lead ores. See ANGLESITE, CERUSSITE, CROCOITE, GALENA, LINARITE, PYROMORPHITE, VANADINITE, WULFENITE.

lead phosphate. See PYROMORPHITE.

lead sulphate. $PbSO_4$. Formed as a white precipitate when sulphuric acid is added to a solution of a lead salt. See ANGLESITE.

lead sulphide. Found in nature as GALENA.

lead vanadate. See VANADINITE.

lechatelierite. A name sometimes applied to naturally fused amorphous silica, such as that which occurs as fulgurites.

lechosos opal. A variety of precious opal exhibiting a deep-green play of colour.

lepidocrocite. An orthorhombic hydrous oxide of iron ($Fe_2O_3 \cdot H_2O$), occurring as scaly blood-red crystals, associated with limonite, in iron ores.

lepidolite. See LITHIA MICA.

lepidomelane. A variety of biotite, rich in iron, and jet-black in colour, occurring commonly in igneous rocks.

leucite. A grey silicate of potassium and aluminium, closely related in chemical composition to orthoclase, but containing less silica. Two varieties occur in rocks: a low-temperature form crystallising in the orthorhombic system, the shape being almost identical with the icositetra-hedron; and a high-temperature form, which is cubic. Occurs in igneous rocks, particularly lavas, of intermediate and basic composition, as for example at Vesuvius.

leucoxene. An opaque whitish mineral formed as a decomposition product of ilmenite; believed to be a variety of sphene.

libethenite. An orthorhombic hydrous phosphate of copper, occurring rarely as olive-green crystals in the oxide zone of metalliferous lodes.

lightning tubes. See FULGURITES.

lignite. This is dull-brown compact fossil wood, representing one stage in the conversion of plant remains into coal. In this country it occurs in the Bovey Tracey

Beds in Devonshire; while it is liable to be found in smaller quantities in lacustrine and estuarine deposits of Mesozoic and Tertiary age. See also BROWN COAL and JET.

lime feldspar. See FELDSPAR, ANORTHITE.

limestone. Sedimentary rock containing carbonate of lime or magnesia to the extent of 50% of the whole. If the carbonate is calcite, the rock is termed *calcite-limestone*; if dolomite is present as well, it is *dolomitic limestone*—or *dolomite rock* if calcite be absent. Limestones are formed by the consolidation of calcareous ooze, which may be chemically precipitated, derived from some pre-existing limestone by the normal processes of rock wastage, or formed by organic agencies. See CALCITE, DOLOMITE ROCK.

lime uranite. See URANITE (LIME).

limonite. A brown amorphous hydrated oxide of iron (and an important ore of that metal) occurring as pseudomorphs after magnetite and haematite. Also the chief constituent of bog iron-ore.

linarite. A complex basic sulphate of lead and copper, found in the oxide zone of metalliferous lodes; a deep-blue mineral resembling azurite, and, like it, crystallising in the monoclinic system.

liroconite. A rare ore of copper, sky-blue to green in colour; essentially hydrated oxide of arsenic combined with hydroxide of copper and aluminium.

lithia mica. This is an important member of the mica group of minerals, occurring as pinkish-mauve crystals, or more typically as scaly aggregates, hence the alternative name LEPIDOLITE (from the Greek *lepis, lepidos*, a scale). The composition is complicated, but it is essentially silicate of potassium, lithium, and aluminium.

lithiophilite. Orthorhombic phosphate of lithium and manganese, forming with triphilite a continuously variable series.

lodestone, loadstone. A form of magnetite that exhibits polarity, behaving, when freely suspended, as a magnet. Occurs extensively at Magnet Heights in Sekukuniland (Transvaal) and elsewhere.

lollingite. Arsenide of iron, $FeAs_2$, occurring as steel-grey crystals, prismatic in habit, belonging to the orthorhombic system.

love arrows. See FLÈCHES D'AMOUR.

lustre. This depends upon the quality and amount of light that is reflected from the surface of a mineral. The highest degree of lustre in opaque minerals is *splendent*, the comparable term for transparent minerals being *adamantine* (i.e. the lustre of diamond). *Metallic* and *vitreous* indicate less brilliant lustre, while *pearly, resinous*, and *dull* are self-explanatory terms covering other degrees of lustre.

luxulianite, luxullianite. A rare type of granite in which tourmaline, in stellate groups, replaces the normal coloured minerals, the other essential constituents being red orthoclase, partly replaced by tourmaline, and quartz. The rock is named from Luxulian, the original locality in Cornwall.

Lydian stone, lydite, or touchstone. A highly siliceous rock, normally black in colour, although surface alteration may change this to grey. In England lydite occurs as small pebbles in many of the newer sedimentary rocks; for example, in the London Basin. They are uniformly fine-textured and even-grained. The name *touchstone* has reference to the use of lydite as a streak plate for gold; the colour left on the stone after rubbing the metal across it indicates to the experienced eye the amount of alloy.

M

Madagascar topaz. See CITRINE.

Madeira topaz. A form of SPANISH TOPAZ.

mafic. A mnemonic term for the ferromagnesian and other nonfelsic minerals actually present in an igneous rock.

magnesia-alum. See PICKERINGITE.

magnesian spinel. See SPINEL.

magnesite. Carbonate of magnesium, crystallising in the trigonal system. Magnesite is a basic refractory used in open-hearth and other high-temperature furnaces; it is resistant to attack by basic slag.

magnesium. Symbol, Mg. A metallic element in the second group of the periodic system. At. no. 12, at. wt. 24·32, m.p. 649° C., specific electrical resistivity 4·46 microhms per c.c., b.p. 1120° C. at 760 mm., density 1·75 grams per c.c., latent heat of fusion 46·5 cal. per gram at 644°. Only found in nature as compounds. The metal is a brilliant white in colour, and magnesium ribbon burns in air, giving an intense white light, rich in ultra-violet rays.

magnesium carbonate. See MAGNESITE.

magnesium mica. See PHLOGOPITE.

magnesium orthodisilicate. Occurs in nature as SERPENTINE.

magnetic pyrite. See PYRRHOTITE.

magnetite or **magnetic iron-ore.** An important ore of iron, ferrosoferric oxide, Fe_3O_4, probably consisting of iron sesquioxide and ferrous oxide, which crystallises in the cubic system. It has the power of being attracted by a magnet, but it has no power to attract particles of iron to itself, except in the form of lodestone.

malachite. One of the basic cupric carbonates, $CuCO_3 \cdot Cu(OH)_2$. It is a common ore of copper, and occurs typically in the oxidation zone of copper deposits.

manaccanite. Sand composed of ILMENITE, found at Manaccan, Cornwall.

mangan-blende. See ALABANDITE.

mangan-epidote. See PIEDMONTITE.

manganese carbonate. See RHODOCHROSITE.

manganese oxides. See MANGANITE, PYRO-LUSITE, PSILOMELANE.

manganese silicate ($MnSiO_3$). See RHODONITE.

manganese spar. See RHODOCHROSITE.

manganese tungstate. See WOLFRAMITE.

manganite. A black hydrated oxide of manganese, crystallising in the orthorhombic system. It is a minor ore of manganese.

manganophyllite. A biotite containing manganese; it occurs in aggregations of thin scales and has a colour ranging from bronze to copper-red.

manganosite. The protoxide of manganese which crystallises in the cubic system.

marcasite. (1) White iron pyrite. This is a disulphide of iron which crystallises in the orthorhombic system. It resembles iron pyrite, but has a lower specific gravity, is less stable, and is paler in colour when in a fresh condition.—(2) In the gemstone trade *marcasite* is pyrite, polished steel, or even white metal.

marekanite. A rhyolitic perlite broken down into more or less rounded pebbles; named from the type locality, Marekana river, Eastern Siberia.

margarite. Hydrated silicate of calcium and aluminium, crystallising in the monoclinic system.

marialite. Silicate of aluminium and sodium with sodium chloride, crystallising in the tetragonal system. It is one of the species in the isomorphous series of the scapolite group.

marmatite. A ferruginous variety of BLENDE; it contains up to 20% of iron.

martite. Sesquioxide of iron (Fe_2O_3), crystallising in the cubic system like magnetite (Fe_3O_4), and believed to be pseudomorphous after magnetite, and in part perhaps after iron pyrite.

maskelynite. A mineral which occurs in colourless isotropic grains in meteorites and has a composition near labradorite. It probably represents re-fused feldspar.

massicot. Lead monoxide which crystallises in the orthorhombic system. It is a rare mineral of secondary origin, associated with galena.

massive minerals. If the crystalline grains are so small that they cannot be distinguished except under the high powers of a microscope, the structure is described as compact, and the mineral is said to be massive.

matlockite. Oxychloride of lead (PbO·PbCl₂) which occurs in tabular tetragonal crystals.

Matura diamonds. Colourless zircons from Ceylon, which on account of their brilliancy are useful as gemstones.

meerschaum. One of the hydrated silicates of magnesium. It is clay-like, and is shown microscopically to be a mixture of a fibrous mineral called parasepiolite and an amorphous mineral β-sepiolite. It is used for making pipes, and formerly was used in Morocco as a soap. Also called SEPIOLITE.

meionite. Silicate of aluminium and calcium, together with calcium carbonate, which crystallises in the tetragonal system. It is a species of the isomorphous series forming the scapolite group.

melaconite. Cupric oxide crystallising in the triclinic system. It is a black earthy material found as an oxidation product in copper veins. See also TENORITE.

melanite. Silicate of calcium and iron, crystallising in the cubic system. It is a black variety of garnet.

melanterite. Hydrous ferrous sulphate which crystallises in the monoclinic system. It usually results from the decomposition of iron pyrite or marcasite. Also called COPPERAS.

melilite. A complex mineral crystallising in the tetragonal system and consisting of a mixture of two minerals in isomorphous series—gehlenite (calcium aluminium silicate) and akermanite (calcium magnesium silicate). Melilite occurs as a component of certain recent basic eruptive rocks.

mendipite. Oxychloride of lead, 2PbO·PbCl₂, which crystallises in the orthorhombic system; found in the Mendip Hills of Somerset.

menilite. An alternative and more attractive name for LIVER-OPAL; it is a grey or brown variety of opal.

mercury. A white metallic element which is liquid at atmospheric temperature. Chemical symbol Hg, at. wt. 200·61, at. no. 80, sp. gr. at 20° C. 13·546, m.p. − 38·5° C., b.p. 356·7° C., specific electrical resistivity 95·8 microhms per cu. cm. A solvent for most metals, the products being called *amalgams*. Native mercury occurs only in small quantities, usually in cavities of mercurial ores, by far the most important of which is CINNABAR. Also called QUICKSILVER.

mercury sulphide. See CINNABAR, META-CINNABARITE.

mesitite. A variety of MAGNESITE containing from 30-50% of iron carbonate.

mesolite. A mineral intermediate in composition between NATROLITE and SCO-LECITE. Crystallises in the monoclinic system, and occurs in amygdaloidal basalts and similar rocks.

mesotype. A name given by Haüy to NATROLITE, because its form is intermediate between the forms of stilbite and analcite.

metacinnabarite. Mercuric sulphide. In composition similar to CINNABAR, but occurs in black tetrahedral (cubic) crystals (also massive).

metallic elements. This group includes the native metals copper, silver, gold, and platinum, and the so-called semi-metals arsenic, antimony, and bismuth.

metallic lustre. A degree of lustre exhibited by certain opaque minerals, comparable with that of polished steel.

metamorphism. The sum of the processes which can operate within the earth's crust and transform a rock into a well-characterised new type.

meteorites. Mineral aggregates of cosmic origin which reach the earth from interplanetary space. See AEROLITES, PALLASITE.

miarolitic structure. A structure found in an igneous rock, consisting of irregularly shaped cavities into which the constituent minerals may project as perfectly terminated crystals.

mica. A group of minerals which crystallise in the monoclinic system; they have similar chemical compositions and highly perfect basal cleavage. See also BIOTITE, LEPIDOMELANE, LITHIA MICA, MUSCOVITE, PHLOGOPITE.

micaceous iron-ore. A variety of specular iron-ore (Fe_2O_3) which is foliated or which simulates mica in habit.

microcline. This is a silicate of potassium and aluminium which crystallises in the triclinic system. See also POTASH FELDSPAR.

microlite. A minute crystal.

microlite. A mineral which is essentially a pyrotantalate of calcium, but which frequently contains niobium, fluorine, and a variety of bases. It crystallises in the cubic system.

microperthite. A feldspar which consists of interlaminations of orthoclase and albite on a microscopic scale.

millerite. 'Capillary pyrite.' Sulphide of nickel, crystallising in the hexagonal system. It usually occurs in very slender crystals and often in delicately radiating groups.

mimetite or mimetesite. Arsenate of lead with chloride of lead, which crystallises in the hexagonal system. It is usually found in lead deposits which have undergone a secondary alteration.

mineral. A body produced by processes of inorganic nature. It has usually a definite chemical composition, a certain characteristic atomic structure, which is expressed in its crystalline form, and other physical properties. Substances such as amber, lignite, coal, though of organic origin, have some characteristics in common with true minerals, and, because of their economic importance, are usually included in the consideration of minerals.

mineral caoutchouc. See ELATERITE.

mineral-pitch. See ASPHALT.

mineralogy. The scientific study of minerals.

minverite. A basic intrusive rock, in essentials a dolerite, containing a brown, soda-rich hornblende; named from the type-locality, St Minver, Cornwall.

mirabilite. See GLAUBER SALT.

mispickel. Sulpharsenide of iron, FeAsS, crystallising in the orthorhombic system. It is used as an ore of arsenic. Also called ARSENICAL PYRITE, ARSENOPYRITE.

mizzonite. One of the series of minerals forming the scapolite group, consisting of a mixture of the meionite and mariolite molecules. It includes those minerals with 54-57% silica, and occurs in clear crystals in the ejected masses on Mte. Somma, Vesuvius. Also called DIPYRE, DIPYRITE.

Mocha stone. See MOSS AGATE.

Mohs' scale of hardness. A scale introduced by Mohs to measure the hardness of minerals. See HARDNESS.

moldavite. See TEKTITES.

molybdenite. Disulphide of molybdenum, MoS_2, crystallising in the hexagonal system. It is the most common ore of molybdenum, but never occurs in large quantities.

molybdite. A hydrous ferric molybdate which crystallises in the orthorhombic system. It is commonly impure and occurs in small amounts as an oxidation product of molybdenite. Also called MOLYBDIC OCHRE, FERRIMOLYBDITE.

monazite. An accessory mineral, crystallising in the monoclinic system. One of the chief sources of thorium used in the manufacture of gas mantles. The mineral frequently contains the rare earth metals, principally cerium and lanthanum.

monoclinic system. The style of crystal architecture in which the three crystal axes are of unequal lengths, having one of their intersections oblique and the other two at right-angles. Also called OBLIQUE SYSTEM.

montebrasite. The name given to AMBLYGONITE when there is an increase of hydroxyl.

monticellite. A silicate of calcium and magnesium which crystallises in the orthorhombic system. It occurs very often in crystals embedded in limestones.

montmorillonite. A hydrated silicate of aluminium, one of the important clay-minerals and the chief constituent of bentonites and fuller's earth.

moonstone. A variety of adularia or microperthite which often possesses a bluish pearly opalescence. It is used as a gemstone.

morganite. A rose-coloured variety of beryl (named after J. Pierpont Morgan), obtained chiefly from California and Madagascar; used as a gemstone. Also called VEROBYERITE.

moss agate. A variegated cryptocrystalline silica containing visible impurities, as manganese dioxide, in moss-like or dendritic form. Also called MOCHA STONE.

mossite. See TAPIOLITE.

mother of emerald. A variety of PRASE, a leek-green quartz owing its colour to included fibres of actinolite; thought at one time to be the mother-rock of emerald.

mottramite. A variety of descloizite in which the zinc element is almost entirely replaced by copper.

mountain cork. A variety of asbestos

which consists of thick interlaced fibres. It is light and will float, and is of a white or grey colour.

mountain leather. A variety of asbestos which consists of thin flexible sheets made of interlaced fibres.

mountain wood. A compact fibrous variety of asbestos looking like dry wood.

mud. A fine-grained unconsolidated rock, of the clay grade, often with a high percentage of water present. It may consist of several minerals.

Müller's glass. See HYALITE.

mullite. A silicate of aluminium, closely similar to sillimanite but with formula $3Al_2O_3 \cdot 2SiO_2$. It occurs in contact-altered argillaceous rocks.

mundic. See IRON PYRITE.

muscovite. This is the common or white mica; for the most part an orthosilicate of potassium and aluminium, crystallising in the monoclinic system. It can be used as an insulator (not above 600° C., when its water of composition is driven off; see PHLOGOPITE), as a lubricant, or for non-inflammable windows.

Muscovy glass. Formerly a popular name for MUSCOVITE.

N

nacreous. A term applied to the lustre of certain minerals, usually on crystal faces parallel to a good cleavage, the lustre resembling that of pearls.

nacrite. A species of clay mineral, identical in composition with kaolin, from which it differs in certain optical characters and in atomic structure.

nail-head-spar. Name for CALCITE.

napoleonite. A gabbro containing spheroidal structures, about one inch in diameter, which consist of alternating shells essentially of hornblende and feldspars. Also CORSITE.

native. Said of naturally occurring metals and salts :—e.g. *native* gold, *native* barium sulphate.

natrojarosite. Hydrous sulphate of sodium and iron, crystallising in the trigonal system.

natrolite. One of the zeolites, hydrated silicate of sodium and aluminium crystallising in the orthorhombic system. It usually occurs in prismatic crystals which are slender or acicular and closely resemble tetragonal crystals.

natural glass. Magma of any composition is liable to occur in the glassy condition if cooled sufficiently rapidly. Acid (i.e. granitic) glass is commoner than basic (i.e. basaltic) glass; the former is represented among igneous rocks by pumice, obsidian, and pitchstone; the latter by tachylyte. Natural quartz glass occurs in masses lying on the surface of certain sandy deserts (e.g. the Libyan Desert); while both clay rocks and sandstones are locally fused by basic intrusions. See also BUCHITE, TEKTITES.

nayagite. A sulpho-telluride of lead and gold (sometimes containing antimony) crystallising in the orthorhombic system.

needle stone. A popular term for clear quartz containing acicular inclusions, usually of rutile, but in some specimens, of actinolite. Also called RUTILATED QUARTZ.

nepheline, nephelite. Silicate of sodium and aluminium, $NaAlSiO_4$, which crystallises in the hexagonal system. It is frequently present in igneous rocks with a high soda content and a low percentage of silica.

nephelinite. A fine-grained igneous rock normally occurring as lava flows, and resembling basalt in general appearance; it consists essentially of nepheline and pyroxene, but not of olivine or feldspar. The addition of the former gives *olivine-nephelinite*, and of the latter, *nepheline-tephrite*.

nephrite. An amphibole, one of the minerals grouped under the name of *jade*; consists of compact and fine-grained tremolite or actinolite. It has been widely used for ornaments in the Americas and the East.

New Zealand greenstone. Nephritic 'jade' of gemstone quality, from New Zealand.

niccolite. An arsenide of nickel, NiAs, crystallising in the hexagonal system. It usually contains a little iron, cobalt, and sulphur and is one of the chief ores of metallic nickel. Also erroneously called COPPER NICKEL, KUPFERNICKEL.

nickel antimony glance. Sulphantimonide of nickel, crystallising in the cubic system. Also called ULLMANNITE.

nickel arsenic glance. GERSDORFFITE.

nickel bloom. See ANNABERGITE.

nickeline. An old term for NICCOLITE.

nicopyrite. See PENTLANDITE.

niobite. See COLUMBITE.

nitre. Potassium nitrate crystallising in the orthorhombic system. Also called SALTPETRE. See also CHILE NITRE, SODA NITRE.

norite. A coarse-grained igneous rock of basic composition consisting essentially of plagioclase (near labradorite in composition) and orthopyroxene. Other coloured minerals are usually present in varying amount, notably clinopyroxene, which, however, must not exceed half of the total pyroxene content.

nosean or **noselite.** Silicate of sodium and aluminium with sodium sulphate, crystallising in the cubic system. Occurs in extrusive igneous rocks which are rich in alkalies and deficient in silica, e.g. phonolite.

O

obsidian. A volcanic glass of granitic composition, generally black with vitreous lustre and conchoidal fracture; occurs at Mt. Hecla in Iceland, in the Lipari Isles, and in the Yellowstone Park, U.S.A. A green silica glass found in ploughed fields in Moravia is cut as a gemstone and sold under the name *obsidian*. True obsidian is used as a gemstone and is often termed ICELAND AGATE.

octahedrite. A form of ANATASE (q.v.), crystallising in tetragonal bipyramids (*not* in octahedra—thus the name is a misnomer). It is usually of secondary origin, derived from other titanium-bearing minerals.

odontolite. See BONE TURQUOISE.

oldhamite. Sulphide of calcium, usually found as cubic crystals in meteorites.

oligiste-iron. Specular iron ore. See HAEMATITE.

oligoclase. One of the plagioclase feldspars, consisting of the albite (Ab) and anorthite (An) molecules combined in the proportions of $Ab_9 An_1$ to $Ab_7 An_3$. It is found especially in the more acid igneous rocks.

olivenite. A hydrated arsenate of copper which crystallises in the orthorhombic system. It is a rare green mineral of secondary origin found in copper deposits.

olivine. An orthosilicate of iron and magnesium, crystallising in the orthorhombic system, which occurs widely in the basic and ultramafic igneous rocks, and includes olivine-gabbro, olivine-dolerite, olivine-basalt, peridotites, etc. See CHRYSOLITE. The clear-green variety is used as a gemstone under the name PERIDOT. For *olivine-nephelinite* see NEPHELINITE; and for *iron-olivine* see FAYALITE.

olivine-rock. See DUNITE.

omphacite. An aluminous pyroxene, near diopside in composition, occurring in eclogites as pale-green mineral grains; in a thin section colourless, superficially resembling olivine.

onyx. A cryptocrystalline variety of silica which consists of layers of different colours, white, black, and red, the bands being straight, not curved (as in agate).

onyx marble. Oriental alabaster (see under ALABASTER).

oölith. A more or less spherical concretion of calcium carbonate, chamosite, or dolomite, not exceeding 2 mm. in diameter, usually showing a concentric-layered and/or a radiating fibrous structure.

opal. This is an amorphous variety of silica with a varying amount of water. The transparent coloured varieties, exhibiting opalescence, are highly prized as gemstones. See FIRE OPAL, WOOD OPAL, BLACK OPAL, MENILITE (LIVER OPAL).

opal agate. A variety of opal, of different shades of colour and agate-like in structure.

opal jasper. Opal containing some yellow iron oxide and other impurities; it has the colour of yellow jasper with the lustre of common opal. Also called JASP-OPAL.

opalescence. (1) The milky, iridescent appearance of a solution or mineral due

to the reflection of light from very fine, suspended particles.—(2) The play of colour exhibited by precious opal, due to interference at the surfaces of minutely thin films, the thicknesses of the latter being of the same order of magnitude as the wavelength of light.

ophicalcite. See FORSTERITE-MARBLE.

ophitic texture. A texture characteristic of dolerites in which relatively large pyroxene crystals completely enclose smaller, lath-shaped plagioclases. See also POIKILITIC.

ore. A term applied to metalliferous minerals which are of economic value and can (or may) be profitably exploited. It is extended to non-metals and also to minerals which are potentially valuable.

Oriental alabaster. See under ALABASTER.

Oriental almandine. A trade name for corundum of gemstone quality, which is deep-red in colour, resembling true almandine (a garnet) in this, but no other, respect.

Oriental amethyst, etc. See FALSE AMETHYST, etc.

Oriental cat's eye. See CYMOPHANE.

Oriental emerald. A trade name for corundum, of gemstone quality, resembling true emerald in colour.

Oriental topaz. A variety of the mineral corundum in colour resembling topaz and sold as such.

orpiment. Trisulphide of arsenic, As_2S_3, which crystallises in the monoclinic system. It is commonly associated with realgar, AsS, and is used as a pigment.

orthite. See ALLANITE.

orthoclase. A feldspar, silicate of potassium and aluminium, $KAlSi_3O_8$, crystallising in the monoclinic system; it occurs as an essential constituent in granitic and syenitic rocks, and as an accessory in many other rock types. See also SANIDINE, MICROCLINE.

orthophyric. A textural term applied to medium- and fine-grained syenitic rocks consisting of closely packed orthoclase crystals of stouter build than in the typical trachytic texture.

orthopyroxene. A group of pyroxene minerals crystallising in the orthorhombic system; e.g. enstatite, hypersthene.

orthorhombic system. The style of crystal architecture which is characterised by three crystal axes, at right-angles to each other and all of different lengths. It includes such minerals as olivine, topaz, and barytes.

osmiridium. A very hard, white, naturally occurring alloy of osmium (17-48%) and iridium (49%) containing smaller amounts of platinum, ruthenium, and rhodium.

ottrelite. A manganese-bearing chloritoid mineral, a product of the metamorphism of certain argillaceous sedimentary rocks, named from Ottrez in the Ardennes.

ottrelite-slate. A metamorphic argillaceous rock characterised by abundant crystals of ottrelite.

oxygen. A colourless and odourless gas which supports combustion and is essential for the respiration of most forms of life. Oxygen is the most abundant element, forming 21% by volume of the atmosphere, eight-ninths by weight of water, and nearly one-half by weight of the rocks of the earth's crust.

ozokerite. A mineral paraffin wax, of dark yellow, brown, or black colour, m.p. 55°-110° C., sp. gr. 0·85-0·95, soluble in petrol, benzene, turpentine; it is found in Galicia and near the Caspian Sea. When bleached, it forms CERESINE WAX.

P

pagodite. This is like ordinary massive PINITE in its amorphous compact texture and other physical characters, but contains more silica. The Chinese carve the soft stone into miniature pagodas and images. Also called AGALMATOLITE.

pallasite. A group name for stony meteorites which contain fractured or rounded crystals of olivine in a network of nickel-iron.

paragonite. A silicate of sodium, aluminium, and hydrogen. It is a sodium mica, has a yellowish or greenish colour, and is usually associated with metamorphic rocks.

paramorph. The name given to a mineral species which can change its molecular constitution without any change of chemical substance. See PSEUDOMORPH.

paramudras. Flint nodules of exceptionally large size and doubtful significance occurring in the Chalk exposed on the east coast of England.

pargasite. A monoclinic amphibole closely similar to hornblende but containing a peculiar molecule with fluorine, aluminium, and sodium as its chief constituents. Named from Pargas, Finland.

peacock ore. The name given to BORNITE because it rapidly becomes iridescent from tarnish.

pearl spar. See DOLOMITE.

pea-stone. Same as PISOLITE.

pectolite. A silicate of calcium and sodium, with a variable amount of water, which crystallises in the monoclinic system. It occurs in aggregations like the zeolites in the cavities of basic eruptive rocks.

pegmatite. A term originally applied to granitic rocks characterised by intergrowths of feldspar and quartz, as in graphic granite; now applied to igneous rocks of any composition but of particularly coarse grain, occurring as offshoots from, or veins in, larger intrusive rock bodies, representing a flux-rich residuum of the original magma.

Pélé's hair. Long threads of volcanic glass, which result from jets of lava being blown aside by the wind in the volcano of Kilauea, Hawaii.

pencatite. A crystalline limestone which contains brucite and calcite in approximately equal molecular proportions. Formed by contact-metamorphism from magnesian limestones. See also PREDAZZITE.

pencil-ore. Hard fibrous masses of HAEMATITE that can be split up into thin rods.

pencil stone. The name given to the compact variety of pyrophyllite, used for slate-pencils.

penetration twins. Same as INTERPENETRATION TWINS.

penninite. A silicate of magnesium with chemically combined water. It crystallises in the monoclinic system, but is rhombohedral in habit. It is a member of the chlorite group of minerals.

pentlandite. A sulphide of iron and nickel which crystallises in the cubic system. It commonly occurs intergrown with pyrrhotite, from which it can be distinguished by its octahedral cleavage. Also called NICOPYRITE.

periclase. Native magnesia. Oxide of magnesium, which crystallises in the cubic system. It is commonly found in metamorphosed magnesian limestones, but when exposed to a damp atmosphere it hydrates to the much commoner brucite.

pericline. A variety of ALBITE which usually occurs as elongated crystals which are twinned.

peridot. See OLIVINE; also BRAZILIAN PERIDOT, CEYLONESE PERIDOT.

peridotite. A coarse-grained ultramafic igneous rock consisting essentially of olivine, with other mafic minerals such as hypersthene, augite, biotite, and hornblende, but free from plagioclase. See DUNITE, KIMBERLITE, SCYELITE.

peristerite. A whitish variety of albite, which is beautifully iridescent.

perknite. A family of coarse-grained ultramafic igneous rocks which consist essentially of pyroxenes and amphiboles, but contain no feldspar.

perlite. An acid and glassy igneous rock which exhibits perlitic structure.

perlitic structure. A structure found in glassy igneous rocks, which consists of systems of spheroidal concentric cracks produced during cooling.

perovskite. Titanate of calcium, $CaTiO_3$, which may crystallise in the cubic system or else in the orthorhombic (to which system its optical characters conform). An accessory mineral in melilite-basalt.

perthite. The general name for megascopic intergrowths of potash- and soda-feldspars, both components having been miscible to form a homogeneous compound at high temperatures, but the one having been thrown out of solution at a lower temperature, thus appearing as inclusions in the other. See also MICROPERTHITE.

perthosite. A type of soda-syenite consisting to a very large extent of perthitic feldspars, occurring at Ben Loyal and Loch Ailsh in Scotland.

petalite. A silicate of lithium and aluminium which crystallises in the monoclinic system. Crystals are rare.

petrified wood. Wood which has had its structure replaced by calcium carbonate, silica, or agate in solution. Many of the original minute structures are preserved.

petrography. Systematic description of rocks, based on observations in the field, on hand specimens, and on thin microscopic sections. Cf. PETROLOGY.

petrology. That study of rocks which includes consideration of their mode of origin, present conditions, chemical and mineral composition, their alteration and decay.

petzite. A telluride of silver and gold. It is steel-grey to black and often shows tarnish.

phacellite. See KALIOPHILITE.

phacolite. A mineral of the zeolite group, related to chabazite; so named from its lens-like crystal form. (Gr. *phakos*, a lentil, *lithos*, a stone.)

phanerocrystalline. Said of an igneous rock in which the crystals of all the essential minerals can be discerned by the naked eye.

pharmacolite. A hydrous arsenate of calcium which crystallises in the monoclinic system. It is a product of the late alteration of mineral deposits which carry arsenopyrite and the arsenical ores of cobalt and silver.

pharmacosiderite. Hydrated arsenate of iron. It crystallises in the cubic system, and is a product of the alteration of arsenical ores.

phenacite. An orthosilicate of beryllium, crystallising in the hexagonal system. It is commonly found as a product of pneumatolysis. Sometimes cut as a gem-stone, having great brilliance of lustre but lacking fire. The name (Greek, ' the deceiver ') refers to the frequency with which it has been confused with quartz.

phenocrysts. Large (megascopic) crystals, usually of perfect crystalline shape, found in a fine-grained matrix in igneous rocks. See PORPHYRITIC TEXTURE.

phillipsite. A fibrous zeolite; hydrated silicate of potassium, calcium, and aluminium, usually grouped in the monoclinic system. Some twinned forms possess pseudo-symmetry.

phlogopite. Silicate of potassium, magnesium, aluminium, and hydrogen, crystallising in the monoclinic system. It is a magnesium mica, and is usually a product of metamorphism, being found in crystalline limestone. Phlogopite is not so good as MUSCOVITE at low temperatures, but it keeps its water of composition until 950° C.

phosgenite. A chloro-carbonate of lead, crystallising in the tetragonal system. It is a rare mineral found in association with cerussite.

phosphatic deposits. Beds containing calcium phosphate which are formed especially in areas of low rainfall, and which may be exploited as sources of phosphate.

phosphorescence. The greenish glow observed during the slow oxidation of white phosphorus in the air, and that emitted by certain substances after having been illuminated by visible or ultra-violet rays. It may be regarded as FLUORESCENCE which persists after the exciting radiation has ceased.

phosphorite or rock-phosphate. The fibrous concretionary variety of APATITE.

phyllite. A name which has been used in several different senses: (1) for the pseudohexagonal platy minerals including mica, chlorite, and talc (by some French authors); (2) for argillaceous rocks in a condition of metamorphism between slate and mica-schist (by most English authors). Phyllite in the latter (usual) sense is characterised by a silky lustre due to the minute flakes of white mica which, however, are individually too small to be seen with the naked eye.

pickeringite. Magnesia alum. Hydrated sulphate of aluminium and magnesium, crystallising in the monoclinic system. It usually occurs in fibrous masses, and is formed by the weathering of pyrite-bearing schists.

picotite. A dark-coloured spinel containing iron, magnesium, and chromium.

picrite. A general name for ultramafic coarse-grained igneous rocks, consisting essentially of olivine and other ferro-magnesian minerals, together with a small amount of plagioclase.

picrite-basalt. An unsatisfactory name—used in current geological literature, however—for basalts particularly rich in mafic minerals, thus bearing the same relationship to normal basalts that picrites bear to normal gabbros.

piedmontite. A silicate of calcium, aluminium, manganese, and hydrogen, crystallising in the monoclinic system. Also called MANGAN-EPIDOTE.

pigeonite. One of the pyroxenes, intermediate in composition between clino-enstatite and diopside. It is a mixture of two molecules: a silicate of iron and magnesium, and a silicate of calcium and magnesium. Named from Pigeon Point, Minnesota.

pingos d'agoa. Brazilian name, meaning ' drops of water,' for perfectly colourless and water-clear pebbles of topaz.

pinite. A hydrous silicate of aluminium and potassium which is usually amorphous. It is an alteration product of cordierite, spodumene, feldspar, etc., approximating to muscovite in composition.

pisolite. A type of limestone built of rounded bodies similar to oöliths, but of less regular form and 2 mm. or more in diameter.

pisolitic. A term descriptive of the structure of certain sedimentary rocks containing pisoliths (see PISOLITE above). Calcite-limestones, dolomitic limestones, laterites, iron-ores, and bauxites may be pisolitic.

pistacite. See EPIDOTE.

pitch. A dark-coloured, fusible, more or less solid material, containing bituminous or resinous substances, insoluble in water, soluble in several organic solvents. Usually obtained as the distillation residue of tars. See ASPHALT.

pitchblende. A form of URANINITE. Radium was first discovered in this mineral. This and helium are due to the disintegration of uranium.

pitch-opal. An opal with a pitchy lustre.

pitchstone. A glassy igneous rock which has a pitch-like (resinous) lustre and contains crystallites and microlites. It is usually of acid to subacid composition, and contains a notable amount of water (4% or more).

plagioclase feldspars. An isomorphous series of triclinic minerals which consist of albite and anorthite combined in all proportions, ranging from pure soda feldspar to pure lime feldspar. See FELDSPAR; also ALBITE, ANDESINE, ANORTHITE, LABRADORITE, OLIGOCLASE.

plasma. A bright-green translucent variety of cryptocrystalline silica (chalcedony). It is used as a semi-precious gem.

platinum. A white metallic element in the eighth group of the periodic system. Symbol, Pt. At. no. 78, at. wt. 195·23, sp. gr. at 20° C. 21·4, spec. elec. resistivity at 20° C. 9·97 microhms per cm. cub., m.p. 1773° C., Brinell hardness 47. Platinum is the most important of a group of six closely related rare metals, the others being osmium, iridium, palladium, rhodium, and ruthenium. It is heavy, soft, and ductile, immune to attack by most chemical reagents and to oxidation at high temperatures. Native platinum is usually alloyed with iron, iridium, rhodium, palladium, or osmium, and crystallises in the cubic system.

pleochroic halos. Dark-coloured zones around small inclusions of radio-active minerals which are found in certain crystals, notably biotite.

pleochroism. The property of a mineral by which it exhibits different colours in different crystallographic directions on account of the selective absorption of transmitted light.

pleonaste. Oxide of magnesium, iron, and aluminium, crystallising in the cubic system. It is a member of the spinel group and may be dark-green, brown, or black in colour. Also called CEYLONITE.

plumasite. A very rare rock type consisting essentially of oligoclase and corundum only.

plumbago. GRAPHITE.

plumbojarosite. A basic hydrous sulphate of lead and iron, crystallising in the trigonal system. See JAROSITE.

plush copper ore. See CHALCOTRICHITE.

pneumatolysis. The destructive after-action of the concentrated volatile constituents of a magma, effected after the consolidation of the main body of magma.

poikilitic. Said of a texture in igneous rocks in which small crystals of one mineral are irregularly scattered in larger crystals of another—e.g. small olivines embedded in larger pyroxenes, as in some peridotites.

poikiloblastic. A textural term applicable to metamorphic rocks in which small crystals of one mineral are embedded in large crystals of another. The texture is comparable with the POIKILITIC of igneous rocks.

polianite. Dioxide of manganese, crystallising in the tetragonal system. It is distinguished from PYROLUSITE by its hardness and anhydrous character.

pollucite. A rare alumino-silicate of caesium, occurring as clear colourless cubic crystals in Maine, U.S.A.; used as a gemstone.

polybasite. Sulphide of silver and antimony, crystallising in the monoclinic system. It is found in many silver veins.

polymorphism. The property possessed by certain chemical compounds of crystallising in several forms which are genetically distinct: thus TiO_2 occurs as the mineral species ANATASE, BROOKITE, and RUTILE.

porpezite. A variety of gold which contains up to 10% of palladium.

porphyritic texture. The term applied to the texture of igneous rocks which contain isolated euhedral crystals larger than those which constitute the groundmass in which they are set.

porphyroblastic. A textural term applicable to metamorphic rocks containing conspicuous crystals in a finer groundmass.

porphyry. A general term used rather loosely for igneous rocks which contain relatively large isolated crystals set in a fine-grained groundmass; e.g. *granite-porphyry*. It is better used as a textural qualifier combined with a specific rock name; e.g. *porphyritic microgranite*, a medium- to fine-grained rock of granitic composition with porphyritic texture.

portlandite. Calcium hydroxide, $Ca(OH)_2$, occurring as hexagonal plates in the Chalk-dolerite contact-zone at Scawt Hill, Co. Antrim. Occurs also in Portland cement, hence the name.

potash feldspar. Silicate of aluminium and potassium, $KAlSi_3O_8$, occurring in two distinct crystalline forms—ORTHOCLASE (monoclinic) and MICROCLINE (triclinic). Both are widely distributed in acid and intermediate rocks, especially in granites and syenites and the fine-grained equivalents. See FELDSPAR, GLASSY FELDSPAR, SANIDINE.

potash mica. See MUSCOVITE, SERICITE.

potash-syenite. A syenitic rock characterised by a large excess of potash-feldspar or feldspathoid over soda-feldspar.

potassium alum. A hydrous sulphate of aluminium and potassium, crystallising in the cubic system. It is found in connexion with volcanoes and also as a result of the action of ascending acid waters.

potassium mica. See MUSCOVITE.

potassium nitrate. KNO_3. Salt of potassium and nitric acid. Strong oxidising agent. Known also as NITRE, SALTPETRE.

potstone. A massive variety of TALC, more or less impure.

prase. A translucent and dull leek-green variety of CHALCEDONY.

predazzite, pencatite, brucite-marble. Mixtures of brucite, calcite, periclase, and hydro-magnesite, found originally at Predazzo, Italy; formed from magnesian limestone by contact-metamorphism.

prehnite. A pale-green, hydrous, usually fibrous acid orthosilicate of calcium and aluminium, crystallising in the orthorhombic system. It occurs, with zeolites, in geodes in altered igneous rocks.

pressed amber. See AMBROID.

prismatic system. See ORTHORHOMBIC SYSTEM.

probertite. Hydrated oxide of sodium, calcium, and boron, crystallising in the monoclinic system.

prochlorite. A silicate of magnesium and aluminium with chemically combined water, crystallising in the monoclinic system. It occurs in metamorphic rocks.

proustite. Sulphide of silver and arsenic, Ag_3AsS_3, which crystallises in the trigonal system. It is commonly associated with other silver-bearing minerals. Cf. PYRARGYRITE. Also called RUBY SILVER ORE, LIGHT-RED SILVER ORE.

pseudo-alums. A name sometimes given to double sulphates of the alum type, where there is a bivalent element in place of the univalent element of ordinary alums.

pseudomalachite. Phosphate and hydroxide of copper which resembles malachite and is thought to crystallise in the monoclinic system.

pseudomorph. A mineral whose external form is not the one usually assumed by its particular species, the original mineral having been subjected to molecular replacement by another substance or substances.

psilomelane. One of the oxides of manganese which contains varying amounts of barium, potassium and sodium oxides and water. It is to be regarded as colloidal manganese dioxide, and is used as an ore of manganese.

psittacinite. Vanadate and hydroxide of lead and copper, crystallising in the orthorhombic system.

pucherite. Vanadate of bismuth, crystallising in the orthorhombic system.

purple copper ore. See BORNITE.

pyramidal system. See TETRAGONAL SYSTEM.

pyrargyrite. A sulphide of silver and antimony which crystallises in the trigonal system. It is commonly associated with other silver-bearing minerals; cf. PROUSTITE. Also called RUBY SILVER ORE, DARK-RED SILVER ORE.

pyrite, pyrites. See IRON PYRITE.

pyritohedron. A crystal form of the cubic system, consisting of twelve pentagonal faces; particularly characteristic of pyrite, hence the name. Also called PENTAGONAL DODECAHEDRON.

pyrochlore. Chiefly a niobate of the cerium metals, calcium, and other bases, with titanium, thorium, and fluorine; crystallises in the cubic system. It is found in nepheline-syenites.

pyrochroite. Hydroxide of manganese, crystallising in the trigonal system. It is very similar to brucite.

pyrolusite. Native dioxide of manganese, commonly containing a little water, and crystallising in the orthorhombic system. It often occurs as a pseudomorph after manganite, and is used as an ore of manganese, as an oxidiser, and as a decoloriser. Cf. POLIANITE.

pyromorphite. This is a phosphate and chloride of lead, crystallising in the hexagonal system. It is a mineral of secondary origin, frequently found in lead deposits; a minor ore of lead.

pyrope. The fiery-red garnet; silicate of magnesium and aluminium, crystallising in the cubic system. It is often perfectly transparent and then prized as a gem, being ruby-red in colour.

pyrophyllite. A clay mineral; silicate of aluminium with chemically combined water, crystallising in the orthorhombic system. It occurs in metamorphic rocks; often resembles talc.

pyrostibnite. See KERMESITE.

pyroxene group. A number of mineral species which, although falling into different systems (orthorhombic, monoclinic, and triclinic), are closely related in form, composition, and structure. They are metasilicates of calcium, magnesium, iron with manganese, and less often with sodium, potassium, zirconium, and fluorine. See ACMITE, AEGIRINE, AUGITE, DIALLAGE, DIOPSIDE, ENSTATITE, HYPERSTHENE.

pyroxenite. A coarse-grained, holocrystalline igneous rock, consisting chiefly of pyroxenes. It may contain biotite, hornblende, or olivine as accessories.

pyrrhotite. Ferrous sulphide which contains variable amounts of dissolved sulphur; it crystallises in the hexagonal system. Often contains nickel, and then it becomes a valuable ore. Also called MAGNETIC PYRITE.

Q

quadratic system. The tetragonal system.

quartz. Crystalline silica, SiO_2, occurring either in prisms capped by rhombohedra (low-temperature, α-quartz), or in hexagonal bipyramidal crystals (high-temperature, β-quartz). Widely distributed in rocks of all kinds—igneous, metamorphic and sedimentary; usually colourless and transparent (rock crystal), but often coloured by minute quantities of impurities as in citrine, cairngorm, etc.; also finely crystalline in the several forms of chalcedony, jasper, etc. See also TRIDYMITE, CRISTOBALITE.

quartz-diorite. A coarse-grained holocrystalline igneous rock of intermediate composition, composed of quartz, plagioclase feldspar, hornblende, and biotite, and thus intermediate in mineral composition between typical diorite and granite. This is the TONALITE of some authors.

quartz-dolerite. A variety of dolerite which contains interstitial quartz usually intergrown graphically with feldspar, forming patches of micropegmatite. A dyke-rock of world-wide distribution, well represented by the Whin Sill rock in N. England.

quartz topaz. See CITRINE.

quicksilver. See MERCURY.

R

radium. Symbol, Ra. A radioactive metallic element in the second group of the periodic system. Radium occurs in bröggerite, cleveite, carnotite, pitchblende, in certain mineral springs, and in sea water. Pitchblende and carnotite are the chief sources of supply. Radium is remarkable for spontaneous and uncontrollable disintegration.

rainbow-quartz. See IRIS.

rammelsbergite. Essentially composed of diarsenide of nickel, but with isomorphous diarsenide of iron; crystallises in the orthorhombic system.

rasorite. See KERNITE.

raspberry spar. A form of RHODOCHROSITE.

reaction pair. Two minerals of different composition which exhibit the reaction relationship (see REACTION PRINCIPLE). Thus forsterite at high temperature is converted into enstatite at a lower temperature, by a change in the atomic structure involving the addition of silica from the magma containing it. Forsterite and enstatite form a *reaction pair*.

reaction principle. The conversion of one mineral species stable at high temperature into a different one at lower temperatures.

reaction rim. The peripheral zone of mineral aggregates formed round a mineral or rock fragment by reaction with the magma during the consolidation of the latter. Thus, quartz caught up by basaltic magma is partially resorbed, at the same time being surrounded by a reaction rim of granular pyroxene.

realgar. A bright-red monosulphide of arsenic, which crystallises in the monoclinic system. Cf. ORPIMENT.

red-copper ore. See CUPRITE.

red-iron ore. HAEMATITE, which, when massive, or when crushed to powder, is dull red.

red jasper. See JASPER.

red oxide of copper. See CUPRITE.

red oxide of zinc. See ZINCITE.

red silver ore. For *dark-red silver ore*, see PYRARGYRITE; for *light-red silver ore*, see PROUSTITE.

reddle. A red and earthy variety of haematite, with a certain admixture of clay.

redruthite. A name frequently applied to the mineral CHALCOCITE on account of its occurrence, among other Cornish localities, at Redruth.

regular system. The CUBIC SYSTEM.

retrogressive metamorphism. The changes involved in the conversion of a rock of high metamorphic grade to one of lower grade, through the advent of metamorphic processes less intense than those which determined the original mineral content and texture of the rock.

rhodochrosite. Name for carbonate of manganese which crystallises in the trigonal system, occurring as rose-pink rhombohedral crystals. It is a minor ore of manganese. Also called MANGANESE SPAR.

rhodolite. A gemstone intermediate in chemical composition between pyrope and almandine.

rhodonite. Metasilicate of manganese, crystallising in the triclinic system. It is rose-coloured, and is sometimes used as an ornamental stone.

rhombic system. See ORTHORHOMBIC SYSTEM.

rhombohedral class. A class of the trigonal system, a characteristic form being the RHOMBOHEDRON, which is exhibited by crystals of quartz, calcite, dolomite, etc.

rhombohedron. A crystal form of the trigonal system, bounded by six similar faces, each a rhombus or parallelogram.

rhomb-spar. An old-fashioned synonym for DOLOMITE.

rhyacolite. A glassy type of orthoclase found in the lavas at Vesuvius.

riband jasper. A variety of jasper with colours arranged in parallel bands.

riebeckite. Metasilicate of sodium and iron occurring in soda-rich igneous rocks as black monoclinic prismatic crystals.

ripidolite. A species of the chlorite group of minerals, crystallising in the monoclinic system. It is essentially a hydrated silicate of magnesium and aluminium with ferrous iron.

rock. An aggregate of mineral particles

forming part of the earth's crust (lithosphere). In igneous and metamorphic rocks, it consists of interlocking crystals; in sedimentary rocks, of closely packed mineral grains, often bound together by a natural cement.

rock crystal. The name given to pure, colourless quartz, whether in distinct crystals or not; particularly applicable to quartz of the quality formerly used in making lenses.

rock-forming minerals. The minerals which occur as the dominant constituents of igneous rocks, including quartz, feldspars, feldspathoids, micas, amphiboles, pyroxenes, and olivine.

rock meal. A white and light variety of calcium carbonate, resembling cotton; it becomes a powder on the slightest pressure.

rock milk. A very soft white variety of calcium carbonate which breaks easily in the fingers; it is sometimes deposited in caverns or about sources holding lime in solution. Also called AGARIC MINERAL.

rock-phosphate. See PHOSPHORITE.

rock salt. See HALITE.

rock soap. See STEATITE.

romeite. Naturally occurring antimonite of calcium.

roscoelite. This mineral is essentially MUSCOVITE in which vanadium has partly replaced the aluminium. Its colour is clove-brown to greenish-brown.

rose opal. A variety of opaque common opal having a fine red colour. Cf. the transparent FIRE OPAL.

rose quartz. A variety of quartz of a rose-pink colour, due probably to titanium in minute quantity. The colour is destroyed by exposure to strong sunlight. See also BOHEMIAN RUBY.

rose-topaz. The yellow-brown variety of topaz changed to rose-pink by heating. These crystals often contain inclusions of liquid carbon dioxide.

roumanite. Opal, of gemstone quality, obtained from Roumania.

rubellite. The red transparent variety of tourmaline, used as a semi-precious gemstone.

rubicelle. A yellow or orange-red variety of spinel; an aluminate of magnesium.

ruby. The blood-red variety of the mineral corundum, the oxide of aluminium (Al_2O_3), which crystallises in the trigonal system. Also called TRUE RUBY (to distinguish it from the various types of FALSE RUBY) and ORIENTAL RUBY, though the adjective *Oriental* is quite unnecessary, since it merely stresses the fact that rubies come from the East (Burma, Siam, Ceylon, Afghanistan). See also BALAS RUBY, RUBY SPINEL.

ruby-copper. See CUPRITE.

ruby silver ore. See PROUSTITE, PYRARGYRITE.

ruby spinel. That variety of magnesian spinel, $MgAl_2O_4$, which has the colour, but none of the other attributes, of true ruby. Also known as SPINEL RUBY, a deceptive misnomer.

runic texture. GRAPHIC TEXTURE.

rutilated quartz. See NEEDLE STONE.

rutile. Dioxide of titanium which crystallises as reddish-brown prismatic crystals in the tetragonal system. It is found in igneous and metamorphic rocks, and is a source of titanium.

S

safflorite. Essentially, diarsenide of cobalt (cf. SMALTITE) but with usually a considerable amount of iron and more rarely a small amount of nickel. It crystallises in the orthorhombic system.

sal ammoniac. Chloride of ammonium, which crystallises in the cubic system. It is found as a white encrustation around volcanoes such as Etna and Vesuvius.

salt. See HALITE.

salt (or saline) lakes. Enclosed bodies of water in areas of inland drainage, whose concentration of salts in solution is much higher than in ordinary river water. See SODA LAKES.

saltpetre. See CHILE NITRE, POTASSIUM NITRATE, SODA NITRE.

sand. A term popularly applied to loose, unconsolidated accumulations of detrital sediment, consisting essentially of rounded grains of quartz. Restricted in sedimentary petrology to sediments whose grains lie between 1 mm. and 0·1 mm. diameter; cf. GRIT. In the mechanical analysis of soil, sand, according to international classification, has a size between 0·02 and 2·0 mm. In coral sand the term implies a grade of sediment the individual particles of which are fragments of coral, not quartz.

sandstones. Compacted and cemented sedimentary rocks, which consist essentially of rounded grains of quartz, between the diameters of 1 mm. and 0·1 mm., with a variable content of ' heavy mineral ' grains. According to the nature of the cementing material, the varieties *calcareous sandstone, ferruginous sandstone, siliceous sandstone* may be distinguished; *glauconitic sandstone, micaceous sandstone*, etc., are so termed from the presence in quantity of the mineral named.

sanidine. A form of potash feldspar identical in chemical composition with orthoclase, but physically different, formed under different conditions and occurring in different rock types. It is the high-temperature form of orthoclase, into which it inverts at 900° C. Occurs in lavas and dyke-rocks.

saphir d'eau. French ' water sapphire.' An intense-blue variety of the mineral cordierite, occurring in water-worn masses in the river gravels of Ceylon; used as a gemstone.

saponite. An amorphous silicate of magnesium and aluminium, occurring as soft soapy masses in cavities in serpentine. BOWLINGITE is the same substance.

sapphire. The fine blue transparent variety of crystalline corundum, of gemstone quality; obtained chiefly from Ceylon, Kashmir, Siam, and Australia. See also BRAZILIAN SAPPHIRE.

sapphire quartz. A very rare indigo-blue variety of silicified crocidolite occurring at Salzburg; used as a semi-precious gemstone. Also known as AZURE QUARTZ and SIDERITE.

sapphirine. A rare alumino-silicate of magnesium occurring at Fiskernäs (Greenland) as disseminated blue grains and occasional monoclinic crystals.

sardonyx. A form of chalcedony in which the alternating bands are brown and white. Cf. ONYX.

satin spar. The name given to the fine fibrous varieties of both calcite and gypsum, the former being harder than the latter.

saussurite. Formerly thought to be one mineral, *saussurite* consists of an aggregate of albite, zoisite, prehnite, with other calcium aluminium silicates and calcite. It results from the alteration of feldspars.

saxonite. A coarse-grained, ultramafic igneous rock, consisting essentially of olivine and orthopyroxene, usually hypersthene. A hypersthene-peridotite.

scale of hardness. See HARDNESS.

scalenohedron. An important form in the rhombohedral system: a solid bounded by twelve scalene triangles, and still showing a three-fold arrangement about the vertical axis.

scapolite. A group of minerals forming an isomorphous series, varying from silicate of aluminium and calcium with calcium carbonate, to silicate of aluminium and sodium with sodium chloride. Common scapolite is intermediate in composition between these two minerals. It crystallises in the tetragonal system and is associated with altered lime-rich igneous and metamorphic rocks. Also known as WERNERITE.

scawtite. A silicate and carbonate of calcium occurring as minute monoclinic crystals in vesicles at the contact of dolerite and chalk at Scawt Hill, Co. Antrim.

scheelite. This is an ore of tungsten formed under pneumatolytic conditions. It occurs in association with granites, having the composition tungstate of calcium, and crystallises in the tetragonal system.

schillerisation. A play of colour (in some cases resembling iridescence due to tarnish) produced by the diffraction of light in the surface layers of certain minerals.

schillerspar. See BASTITE.

schorl. See TOURMALINE.

schorl-rock. A rock composed essentially of aggregates of black tourmaline (schorl) and quartz. A Cornish term for the end-product of tourmalinisation. See also LUXULIANITE.

scolecite. A member of the zeolite group of minerals; a hydrated silicate of calcium and aluminium, occurring usually in fibrous or acicular groups of crystals.

Scotch topaz. A term applied in the gemstone trade to yellow transparent quartzes, resembling Brazilian topaz in colour, used for ornamental purposes. See CITRINE, CAIRNGORM.

scyelite. A coarse-grained ultramafic igneous rock, named from the original locality at Loch Scye in Caithness, Scotland; it consists essentially of mafic minerals including serpentine pseudomorphs after olivine set poikilitically in large amphibole crystals associated with large bronze mica crystals. A mica-hornblende-peridotite.

secondary enrichment. The name given to the addition of minerals to, or the change in the composition of the original minerals in, an ore body, either by precipitation from downward-percolating waters or upward-moving gases and solutions. The net result of the changes is an increase in the amount of metal present in the ore at the level of secondary enrichment.

selenite. The name given to the colourless and transparent variety of GYPSUM which occurs as distinct monoclinic crystals, especially in clay rocks.

senarmontite. The trioxide of antimony, crystallising in the cubic system.

sepiolite. See MEERSCHAUM.

sericite. A white potash-mica, like muscovite in chemical composition and general characters but occurring as a secondary mineral, often as a decomposition product of orthoclase.

serpentine. One of the hydrated silicates of basic and ultrabasic igneous rocks which, as a result of autometamorphism, have had their coloured silicates converted in large measure into serpentine. Such serpentines are usually dark green, streaked and blotched with red iron oxide, whitish talc, etc.

serpentine. A hydrated silicate of magnesium which crystallises in the monoclinic system, but as pseudomorphs only. It is always of secondary origin. The translucent varieties are used for ornamental purposes; those with a fibrous habit are called asbestos. See ASBESTOS, CHRYSOTILE.

serpentine-asbestos. See CHRYSOTILE.

serpentine-jade. A variety of the mineral serpentine, resembling bowenite, occurring in China; used as an ornamental stone.

serpentinisation. A type of autometamorphism effected by magmatic water, which results in the replacement of the original mafic silicates by the mineral serpentine (bastite, chrysotile) and secondary fibrous amphibole (tremolite, actinolite).

siderite. A general term for meteoric iron, which usually consists of nickel-iron.

siderite. (1) See CHALYBITE.—(2) See SAPPHIRE QUARTZ.

silica. Dioxide of silicon, SiO_2, which occurs in the crystalline forms as quartz, cristobalite, tridymite; as cryptocrystalline chalcedony; as amorphous opal; and as an essential constituent of the silicate groups of minerals. Used in the manufacture of glass and refractory materials.

silica glass. Fused quartz, occurring in shapeless masses on the surface of the Libyan Desert, in Moravia, in parts of Australia, and elsewhere; believed to be of meteoric origin. See TEKTITES.

silicates. The salts of the silicic acids, the largest group among minerals; of widely different, and in some cases extremely complex, composition, but all containing silica as an essential component. The micas, amphiboles, pyroxenes, feldspars, and garnets are examples of groups of rock-forming silicates.

siliceous sinter. Cellular quartz or translucent to opaque opal, found as incrustations or fibrous growths and deposited from thermal waters containing silica or silicates in solution. Also GEYSERITE.

silicon. Symbol, Si. A non-metallic element in the fourth group of the periodic system. At. no. 14, at. wt. 28·06, valency 4. Amorphous silicon is a brown powder; sp. gr. 2·35. Crystalline silicon is grey; sp. gr. 2·42, m.p. 1420° C., b.p. 2600° C. This element is the second most abundant, silicates being the chief constituents of many rocks, clays, and soils.

silicon dioxide. See SILICA.

silk. A sheen resembling that of silk, exhibited by some corundums, including ruby, and due to minute tubular cavities in parallel orientation. The colour of such stones is paler than normal by reason of the inclusions.

sillimanite. See FIBROLITE.

silver. A pure-white native metallic element in the first group of the periodic system. Chem. symbol Ag, at. wt. 107·88, at. no. 47, sp. gr. at 20° C. 10·5, m.p. 960° C., b.p. 1955° C., casting temp. 1030-1090° C., Brinell hardness 37, specific electrical resistivity 1·62 microhms per cm. cub. The metal is not oxidised in air. Occurs massive, or assumes arborescent or filiform shapes. Native silver often has variable admixture of other metals—gold, copper, or sometimes platinum.

silver amalgam. A solid solution of mercury and silver, which crystallises in the cubic system. The percentage of silver is usually about 26%, but in the variety *arquerite* reaches 86%. It is of rare occurrence, and is found scattered either in mercury or silver deposits.

silver bromide, silver chloride, silver fluoride, silver iodide. See SILVER HALIDES.

silver glance. See ARGENTITE.

silver halides. Silver bromide, AgBr;

silver iodide, AgI; silver chloride, AgCl; and silver fluoride, AgF. The bromide and chloride are sensitive to light and are of basic importance in photography.

silver lead ore. The name given to galena containing silver. When 1% or more of silver is present it becomes a valuable ore of silver. Also called ARGENTIFEROUS GALENA.

sinter. To coalesce into a single mass under the influence of heat, without actually liquefying. See SILICEOUS SINTER.

skeleton crystals. Imperfect crystals of very minute size occurring in glassy igneous rocks; often merely three-dimensional frameworks, the interstices in which would have been filled in under conditions of slower cooling. See also DENDRITE.

skutterudite. Grey or whitish arsenide of cobalt, which crystallises in the cubic system and sometimes assumes a massive granular habit.

smaltite, smaltine. Essentially the diarsenide of cobalt, with some iron and nickel, crystallising in the cubic system. Cloanthite (diarsenide of nickel) is also invariably present, and the two species graduate into each other; occur in veins; ores of cobalt and nickel.

smaragdite. A fibrous green amphibole, replacive after the pyroxene, omphacite, in such rocks as eclogite.

smithsonite. Carbonate of zinc, crystallising in the trigonal system. It occurs in veins and beds and in calcareous rocks, and is commonly associated with hemimorphite. The honeycombed variety is known as *drybone ore*. The name CALAMINE is frequently used in Britain, but not in U.S.A.

smoky-quartz. See CAIRNGORM.

soapstone. See STEATITE.

soda feldspar, soda-lime feldspar. See FELDSPAR.

soda lakes. Salt lakes the water of which contains a high content of sodium salts (chiefly chloride, sulphate, and acid carbonate). These salts also occur as an efflorescence around the lakes.

sodalite. This is a cubic feldspathoid mineral, essentially silicate of sodium and aluminium with sodium chloride, occurring in certain alkali-rich syenitic rocks.

soda nitre. Nitrate of sodium, crystallising in the trigonal system. It is found in great quantities in northern Chile, where beds of it are exposed at the surface and are known as CALICHE. Also called CHILE SALTPETRE.

soda-syenite. A syenitic igneous rock containing an excess of soda-feldspar or feldspathoid. Cf. POTASH-SYENITE.

sodium aluminium fluoride. See CRYOLITE.

sodium chloride. See HALITE.

Spanish topaz. A trade name for orange-brown quartz, the colour resembling that of the honey-brown Brazilian topaz. It is often amethyst which has been heat-treated. See CITRINE.

spar. Any non-metallic mineral with a good cleavage; e.g. calcite or celestine.

spar, Iceland. See ICELAND SPAR.

spartalite. An old name for ZINCITE.

spathic iron. See CHALYBITE.

spear pyrites. The name given to twin crystals of marcasite which show re-entrant angles, in form somewhat like the head of a spear.

specular iron. The name given to a crystalline rhombohedral variety of haematite which possesses a splendent metallic lustre often showing iridescence.

sperrylite. Diarsenide of platinum, crystallising in the cubic system. It has a brilliant metallic lustre and is tin-white in colour.

spessartite, spessartine. Manganese garnet; silicate of manganese and aluminium, crystallising in the cubic system. Usually contains a certain amount of either ferrous or ferric iron. The colour is dark red, sometimes having a tinge of violet or brown. See GARNET.

sphalerite. See BLENDE.

sphene. See TITANITE.

spheroidal structure. A structure exhibited by certain igneous rocks, which appear to consist of large rounded masses, surrounded by concentric shells of the same material. Presumably a cooling phenomenon, comparable with perlitic structure, but on a much bigger scale, and exhibited by crystalline, not glassy, rocks.

spilite. A fine-grained igneous rock of basaltic composition, generally highly vesicular and containing the soda feldspar, albite. The pyroxenes or amphiboles are usually altered. These rocks are frequently developed as submarine lava-flows and exhibit pillow structure.

spinel. A group of closely related minerals crystallising, usually in octahedrons, in the cubic system. They occur typically as products of contact metamorphism of impure dolomitic limestones, and less commonly as accessory minerals in igneous rocks of basic composition. Chemically, spinels are aluminates, chromates or ferrates of magnesium, iron, zinc, etc., and are distinguished as *iron spinel* (hercynite), *zinc spinel* (gahnite), *chrome spinel* (picotite), and *magnesian spinel*. See also RUBY SPINEL, BALAS RUBY, CHROMITE.

spodumene or **triphane.** A silicate of aluminium and lithium which crystallises in the monoclinic system. It usually occurs in granite-pegmatites, often in very large crystals. The rare emerald-green variety HIDDENITE and the clear lilac-coloured variety KUNZITE are used as gems.

spurrite. A carbonate and silicate of calcium, $2Ca_2SiO_4 \cdot CaCO_3$, occurring somewhat rarely in limestones containing silica in the metamorphic aureoles round igneous intrusions, as at Scawt Hill, Antrim.

stalactite. A concretionary deposit of calcium carbonate which is formed by percolating solutions and hangs icicle-like from the roofs of limestone caverns and analogous places.

stalagmite. A concretionary deposit of calcium carbonate, precipitated from dripping solutions on the floors and walls of limestone caverns. Stalagmites are often complementary to stalactites, and may grow so that they eventually join with these.

stannite. A sulpho-stannate of copper, iron, and sometimes zinc, which crystallises in the tetragonal system. It usually occurs in tin-bearing veins, having been deposited from hot ascending solutions. Also called TIN PYRITES, BELL-METAL ORE.

star ruby, —sapphire, —topaz, —quartz. The prefix 'star' has reference to the narrow-rayed star of light exhibited by varieties of the minerals named. The star is seen to best advantage when they are cut *en cabochon*. It is caused by reflections from exceedingly fine inclusions lying in certain planes. See also ASTERISM.

stassfurtite. A massive variety of boracite which sometimes has a subcolumnar structure and resembles a fine-grained white marble or granular limestone. See BORACITE.

staurolite. A complex silicate of aluminium and iron with chemically combined water, commonly occurring as brown cruciform twins, and crystallising in the orthorhombic system. It is usually found in metamorphic rocks. Occasionally a transparent stone is cut as a gemstone. Also called STAUROTIDE.

steatite or **soapstone.** A coarse, massive, or granular variety of talc, greasy to the touch. On account of its softness it is readily carved into ornamental objects. Fired at 800 to 1000° C., it becomes very hard and strong. Used in the making of sparking-plug insulators and giant high-voltage insulators.

stephanite. A sulphide of silver and antimony which crystallises in the orthorhombic system. It is usually associated with other silver-bearing minerals and is deposited from ascending solutions. Also called BRITTLE SILVER ORE.

sterlingite. See ZINCITE.

stibnite. Native trisulphide of antimony which crystallises in grey metallic prisms in the orthorhombic system. It is sometimes auriferous and also argentiferous. It is widely distributed but not in large quantity, and is the chief source of antimony. Formerly called ANTIMONY GLANCE. See ANTIMONITE.

stilbite. One of the zeolites; silicate of aluminium, calcium, and sodium with chemically combined water; crystallises in the monoclinic system, the crystals frequently being grouped in sheaf-like aggregates. Found both in igneous rock cavities and in metamorphic rocks. Also called DESMINE.

stockwork. An irregular mass of interlacing veins of ore.

stony meteorites. Those meteorites which consist essentially of rock-forming silicates. See AEROLITE, ACHONDRITE, CHONDRITE.

streak. The name given to the colour of the powder obtained by scratching a mineral with a knife or file or by rubbing the mineral on paper or an unglazed porcelain surface (*streak plate*).

stream tin. Cassiterite occurring as derived grains in sands and gravels in the beds of rivers.

striae or striations. Surface markings occurring on the faces of some crystals, taking the form of parallel lines; caused by oscillation between two crystal forms.

strontianite. Carbonate of strontium, crystallising in the orthorhombic system. Its colour varies from pale green or grey to brown, and it is associated with limestones and less frequently with eruptive rocks.

succinite. (1) A variety of AMBER, separated mineralogically because it yields succinic acid.—(2) An amber-coloured garnet of the grossularite species.

sulphate of iron. See MELANTERITE.

sulphate of lead. See ANGLESITE.

sulphate of lime. See GYPSUM.

sulphate of strontium. See CELESTINE.

sulphur. A common non-metallic element in the sixth group of the periodic system. At. no. 16, at. wt. 32·06, valencies 2, 4, 6, symbol S. Rhombic (α-) sulphur is a lemon-yellow powder; m.p. 112·8° C., sp. gr. 2·07. Monoclinic (β-) sulphur has a deeper colour than the rhombic form; m.p. 119·0° C., sp. gr. 1·96, b.p. 444·6° C.

sunstone. See AVENTURINE FELDSPAR.

Swiss lapiz. A fraudulent imitation of lapis-lazuli, obtained by staining pale-coloured jasper or ironstone with ferrocyanide. Also known as GERMAN LAPIZ.

syenite. A coarse-grained igneous rock composed essentially of alkali-feldspar to the extent of at least two-thirds of the total, with a variable content of mafic minerals, of which common hornblende is characteristic.

sylvanite. Telluride of gold and silver, which crystallises in the monoclinic system and is usually associated with igneous rocks and, in veins, with native gold. It is used as an ore of gold. See also GRAPHIC TELLURIUM.

sylvinite. A general name for mixtures of the two salts sylvite and halite, the latter predominating.

sylvite. Chloride of potassium, which crystallises in the cubic system. It occurs as a sublimation product near volcanoes, and is a source of potash compounds used as fertilisers.

symmetry. The quality possessed by crystalline substances by virtue of which they exhibit a repetitive arrangement of similar faces. This is a result of their peculiar internal atomic structure, and the feature is used as a basis of crystal classification.

syngenetic. A category of ore bodies comprising all those which were formed contemporaneously with the enclosing rock. Cf. EPIGENETIC, i.e. formed at some subsequent time.

system. A term applied to the sum of the phases which can be formed from one or more components of minerals under different conditions of temperature, pressure, and composition.

systems of crystals. The seven large divisions into which all crystallising substances can be placed, viz. cubic, tetragonal, hexagonal, trigonal, orthorhombic, monoclinic, triclinic. This classification is based on the degree of SYMMETRY displayed by the crystals.

T

tabular spar. See WOLLASTONITE.

taenite. A solid solution of iron in nickel occurring in iron meteorites; it appears as bright white areas on a polished surface.

talc. A soft acid metasilicate of magnesium, $H_2Mg_3Si_4O_{12}$, which crystallises in either the orthorhombic or monoclinic system. It is usually massive and foliated and is a common mineral of secondary origin associated with serpentine and schistose rocks. See STEATITE.

tantalite. Tantalate of iron and manganese, crystallising in the orthorhombic system. It usually has an admixture of the niobate of iron and manganese and the mineral passes from the pure tantalate (tantalite) to the pure niobate (columbite). In some varieties (manganotantalite) the iron is replaced by manganese. It commonly occurs in pegmatite veins.

tapiolite. Niobate and tantalate of iron and manganese. This really forms a variable series of minerals that may be considered as dimorphous with the columbite-tantalite series. The various molecules have been named *tapiolite* (tantalate of iron), MOSSITE (niobate of iron), and IXIOLITE (tantalate of manganese). The minerals crystallise in the tetragonal system.

tarbuttite. The basic phosphate of zinc, which crystallises in the triclinic system. The crystals are often found in sheaf-like aggregates.

tektites. A group term suggested by Suess in 1900 to cover moldavites, billitonites, australites, and to replace the term obsidianite of Walcott (1898). They consist of balls and other spheroidal dumb-bell forms of green and black glass, approximating to obsidian in composition.

telluric bismuth. Bismuth which occurs in the trigonal system and contains a trace of tellurium. See also TETRADYMITE.

tellurium. A metallic element, tin-white

in colour, in the sixth group of the periodic system. Chem. symbol, Te. At. wt. 127·61; at. no. 52; sp. gr. at 20° C. 6·24; m.p. 450° C.; valencies 2, 4, 6. The chief sources are the slimes from copper and lead refineries, and the fine dusts from telluride gold ores.

tennantite. The sulphide of copper and arsenic, which crystallises in the cubic system. This mineral is isomorphous with TETRAHEDRITE. The crystals are frequently dodecahedral and contain antimony, grading into tetrahedrite.

tenorite. Oxide of copper, crystallising in the triclinic system. It occurs in minute black scales as a sublimation product in volcanic regions or associated with copper veins.

tephroite. An orthosilicate of manganese, which crystallises in the orthorhombic system. It forms a member of the isomorphous olivine group, and occurs with zinc and manganese minerals in New Jersey and Sweden.

teschenite. A coarse-grained basic (gabbroic) igneous rock consisting essentially of plagioclase, near labradorite in composition, titanaugite, ilmenite, and olivine (or its decomposition products); primary analcite occurs in wedges between the plagioclase crystals, which it also veins.

tesseral system. CUBIC SYSTEM.

tetradymite. A mineral consisting of bismuth and tellurium. It sometimes contains sulphur and a trace of selenium; crystallises in the trigonal system. Commonly found in gold-quartz veins or in metamorphic rocks.

tetragonal system. The crystallographic system in which all the forms are referred to three axes at right-angles; two are equal and are taken as the horizontal axes, whilst the vertical axis is either longer or shorter than these.

tetrahedrite. A grey sulphide of copper and antimony, $4Cu_2S \cdot Sb_2S_3$, which crystallises in the tetrahedral division of the cubic system, and frequently contains other metals such as bismuth, mercury, silver (as in the old silver-mines of Devon and Cornwall), zinc, and iron. Also called FAHLERZ, FAHLORE, GREY COPPER ORE.

theralite. A coarse-grained, holocrystalline igneous rock composed essentially of the minerals labradorite, nepheline, purple titanaugite, and often with soda-amphiboles, biotite, analcite, or olivine.

thulite. An obsolete name for ZOISITE.

thumb-marked fracture. The minute ripples or ‘ thumb-marks ’ characteristic of the fractured surface of amethyst.

tiger’s eye. A form of silicified crocidolite stained yellow or brown by iron oxide.

tile ore. The earthy brick-red variety of cuprite; often mixed with red iron oxide.

tin. A white metallic element with a yellowish tinge, in the fourth group of the periodic system. Chem. symbol, Sn (Latin *stannum*, tin). At. wt. 118·7; at. no. 50; sp. gr. at 20° C. 7·3; m.p. 232° C.

tin pyrites. See STANNITE.

tin-stone. See CASSITERITE.

tincal. The name given since early times to crude borax obtained from salt lakes.

titaniferous iron ore. See ILMENITE.

titanite. Silicate of calcium and titanium, with iron, or manganese, or yttrium in varying amounts. It crystallises in the monoclinic system as wedge-shaped crystals, usually yellow or brown in colour, and occurs as an accessory component in igneous rocks of intermediate composition and also in metamorphic rocks. Also called SPHENE.

toad’s-eye tin. A variety of CASSITERITE occurring in botryoidal or reniform shapes which show an internal concentric and fibrous structure. Brownish in colour.

tonalite. A coarse-grained igneous rock of dioritic composition carrying quartz as an essential constituent, that is, quartz-mica-diorite. Two varieties are distinguished: soda-tonalite, with albite in excess of anorthite, and lime-tonalite, with anorthite in excess of albite.

topaz. This is a silicate of aluminium and fluorine, usually containing hydroxyl, which crystallises in the orthorhombic system. It usually occurs in granite-like rocks. It is colourless, pale blue, or pale yellow in colour, and is used as a gemstone. Cf. CITRINE, SCOTCH TOPAZ, SPANISH TOPAZ, ORIENTAL TOPAZ.

topazolite. A variety of the calcium-iron garnet ANDRADITE, which has the colour and transparency of topaz. It is sometimes green and the crystals often show a vicinal hexakisoctahedron.

torbanite. A variety of oil shale containing 70-80% of carbonaceous matter, including an abundance of spores. It is dark-brown in colour, and is found at Torbane Hill near Bathgate (Scotland).

torbernite. A beautiful rich-green hydrous phosphate of uranium and copper which crystallises in the orthorhombic system but is pseudo-tetragonal. It occurs associated with AUTUNITE and frequently in parallel growth with it, and also with other uranium minerals. Also called COPPER (or CUPRO-) URANITE.

toscanite. A quartz - bearing trachyandesite.

touchstone. See LYDIAN STONE.

tourmaline. This mineral is a complex silicate of boron and aluminium, with, in addition, magnesium, iron, or the alkali metals, and fluorine in small amounts, which crystallises in the trigonal system. It is usually found in granites or gneisses. The variously coloured and transparent varieties are used as gemstones, under the names *achroite* (colourless), *indicolite* (blue), *rubellite* (pink).

tourmalinisation. The processes whereby minerals or rocks are replaced wholly or in part by tourmaline. These processes result from the invasion by mineralising fluxes and gases.

trachy-andesite. Fine-grained igneous rock,

commonly occurring as lava flows, intermediate in composition between trachyte and andesite, that is, containing both orthoclase and plagioclase in approximately equal amounts.

trachybasalt. A fine-grained igneous rock commonly occurring in lava flows and sharing the mineralogical characters of trachyte and basalt. The rock contains sanidine (characteristic of trachyte) and calcic plagioclase (characteristic of basalt).

trachyte. A fine-grained igneous rock-type, of intermediate composition, in most specimens with little or no quartz, consisting largely of alkali-feldspars (sanidine or oligoclase) together with a small amount of coloured silicates such as diopside, hornblende, or mica.

Transvaal jade. A term applied in the gemstone trade to massive green garnet (grossularite).

tremolite. A silicate of calcium and magnesium which crystallises in the monoclinic system. It is usually grey or white, and occurs in bladed crystals or fibrous aggregates associated with metamorphic rocks. A variety of AMPHIBOLE. See ASBESTOS.

trichite. Thin filament- or hair-like crystallite which occurs in volcanic rocks in irregular or radiating groups.

triclinic system. The crystallographic system which includes all the forms referred to three unequal axes which are not at right-angles.

tridymite. A high-temperature form of silica, SiO_2, crystallising in the orthorhombic system, but possessing pseudo-hexagonal symmetry. The stable form of silica above 870° C. An α and a β form are recognised.

trigonal system. A style of crystal architecture characterised by a principal axis of three-fold symmetry; otherwise resembling the hexagonal system.

trimetric system. ORTHORHOMBIC SYSTEM.

triphane. See SPODUMENE.

tripolite. DIATOMITE.

troctolite. A coarse-grained basic igneous rock, consisting essentially of olivine and plagioclase only. The former mineral occurs as dark spots on a light ground of feldspar, giving the rock a spotted appearance, whence the name TROUTSTONE.

trondhjemite. A coarse-grained igneous rock consisting essentially of plagioclase (ranging from oligoclase to andesine), quartz, and small quantities of biotite, in some instances accompanied, or replaced, by amphibole and pyroxene.

troutstone. See TROCTOLITE.

tungstic ochre or **tungstite.** Trioxide of tungsten, which probably crystallises in the orthorhombic system. It is usually earthy and yellow or greenish in colour, and is a mineral of secondary origin, usually associated with wolframite.

turgite. See HYDROHAEMATITE.

turquoise. This is a hydrous phosphate of aluminium and copper which crystallises in the triclinic system. It is a mineral of secondary origin, found in thin veins or small masses in rocks of various types, and used as a gem. The typical sky-blue colour often disappears when the mineral is dried. Much of the gem turquoise of old was fossil bone of organic origin and not true turquoise.

twin crystal. A crystal which results from the growing together of two crystals in a symmetrical manner.

U

uintaite. A variety of natural asphalt occurring in the Uinta Valley, Utah, as rounded masses of brilliant black solid hydrocarbon. Also called GILSONITE.

ulexite. A hydrous borate of sodium and calcium occurring in saline crusts on alkali flats in arid regions, as in Chile and Nevada, where it forms rounded masses of extremely fine white crystals.

ullmannite. See NICKEL ANTIMONY GLANCE.

ultramafites. Those igneous rocks in which there is an abnormally high content of ferro-magnesian silicates, but which contain no feldspar; subdivided into picrites (with accessory plagioclase), pyroxenites and peridotites.

Uralian emerald. A green variety of andradite garnet, occurring as nodules in ultra-basic rocks in the Nizhni-Tagilsk district of the Urals; used as a semi-precious gemstone, though rather soft. Known also as BOBROVSKA GARNET.

uraninite. Uranate of uranyl, lead, thorium and the metals of the lanthanum and yttrium groups, occurring as opaque cubic crystals, varying in colour from white to black; it appears as an accessory mineral in granitic rocks and in metallic veins. When massive, and probably amorphous, known as PITCHBLENDE.

uranite. For *copper uranite* see TORBERNITE.—LIME URANITE, a tetragonal mineral occurring as thin tabular crystals or in mica-like aggregates of a bright-yellow colour resembling torbernite in composition; a hydrated phosphate of uranium and calcium. See AUTUNITE.

uvarovite. A variety of garnet, of an attractive green colour, essentially silicate of calcium and chromium.

V

valentinite. Trioxide of antimony, Sb_2O_3, occurring as orthorhombic crystals or radiating aggregates; snow-white when pure; formed by the decomposition of other ores of antimony.

vanadinite. Vanadate and chloride of lead, typically forming brilliant blood-red hexagonal crystals or globular masses encrusting other minerals in lead-mines.

variegated copper ore. A popular name for BORNITE. See also PEACOCK ORE.

variscite. A soft-green hydrated phosphate of aluminium ($AlPO_4 \cdot 2H_2O$) occurring as nodular masses in Utah, U.S.A.

vein. An irregular minor intrusion, differing from sills, dykes, cone-sheets, etc., in its relation to the rocks which it penetrates.

verdite. A green rock, consisting chiefly of green mica (fuchsite) and clayey matter, occurring as large boulders in the North Kaap River, South Africa.

vermiculites. A group of hydrous silicates, closely related chemically to the chlorites, and occurring as decomposition products of the micas. When slowly heated they exfoliate and open into long worm-like threads. (L. *vermiculari*, to breed worms.)

verobyerite. See MORGANITE.

vesicular structure. A character exhibited by many extrusive igneous rocks, in which the expansion of gases has given rise to more or less spherical cavities (vesicles). The latter may become filled with such minerals as silica (chalcedony, agate, quartz), zeolites, chlorite, calcite.

vesuvianite. See IDOCRASE.

vicinal faces. Facets modifying normal crystal faces; they usually lie nearly in the plane of the face they modify.

violane. A massive deep-blue form of the pyroxene DIOPSIDE, quarried at San Marcel, Piedmont, Italy.

vitriol, blue, green, white. See BLUE, GREEN, WHITE VITRIOL.

vivianite. A hydrated phosphate of iron, $Fe_3(PO_4)_2 \cdot 8H_2O$, of comparatively rare occurrence in crystallised form, though widely distributed as a pale-blue powder (blue-iron-earth) in peat bogs and bog-iron-ore deposits.

vogesite. A hornblende-lamprophyre, the other essential constituent being orthoclase.

vulpinite. A granular, scaly form of the mineral anhydrite, occurring at Vulpino, Lombardy, where it is cut and polished for ornamental purposes.

vulsinite. A variety of trachy-andesite containing phenocrysts of andesine bordered with sanidine, together with mica, hornblende, and, rarely, olivine, embedded in a groundmass. consisting essentially of sanidine microliths.

W

wad. Bog manganese, hydrated oxide of manganese. See ASBOLANE.

water-chrysolite. MOLDAVITE. See TEKTITES.

water sapphire. See SAPHIR D'EAU.

wavellite. An orthorhombic hydrated phosphate of aluminium, occurring rarely in prismatic crystals, but commonly in flattened globular aggregates, showing a strongly developed internal radiating structure.

websterite. A coarse-grained ultramafic igneous rock, consisting essentially of both ortho- and clino-pyroxenes: a diallage-hypersthene-pyroxenite.

wehrlite. A name, now little used, for ultramafic igneous rocks of coarse grain, consisting essentially of diallage and olivine, i.e. diallage-peridotite.

wernerite. Common SCAPOLITE.

wheel ore. See BOURNONITE.

whewellite. Hydrated calcium oxalate.

white copperas. GOSLARITE.

white iron pyrite. See MARCASITE.

white lead ore. CERUSSITE.

white nickel. CHLOANTHITE.

white sapphire. More reasonably called WHITE CORUNDUM, is the colourless, pure variety of crystallised corundum, Al_2O_3, free from those small amounts of impurities which give colour to the varieties ' ruby ' and ' sapphire.'

white vitriol. A popular name for GOSLARITE. $ZnSO_4 \cdot 7H_2O$.

willemite. Orthosilicate of zinc, Zn_2SiO_4, occurring massive, granular, or in trigonal prismatic crystals, white when pure but commonly red, brown, or green through manganese or iron in small quantities. In New Jersey (Franklin Furnace) and elsewhere it occurs in sufficient quantity to be mined as an ore of lead. Noteworthy as exhibiting an intense bright-yellow fluorescence in ultra-violet light.

withamite. A mineral belonging to the epidote group, named after Dr Witham, of Glencoe, where the mineral was discovered. Contains manganese and is allied to piedmontite.

witherite. Barium carbonate, $BaCO_3$, crystallising in the orthorhombic system as yellowish or greyish-white complicated crystals of hexagonal appearance; also massive. Occurs with galena in the lead mines on Alston Moor and in large quantities near Hexham, Northumberland. An important source of barium.

wolframite. A tungstate of iron and manganese $(FeMn)WO_4$, occurring as brownish-black monoclinic crystals, columnar aggregates, or granular masses in association with tin ores, as in Cornwall. An important ore of tungsten.

wolfsbergite. See CHALCOSTIBITE.

wollastonite. One of the pyroxene group of relatively simple composition, being silicate of calcium, $CaSiO_3$, crystallising in the monoclinic system and occurring in metamorphosed siliceous limestones. It is also represented in the more complicated pyroxenes, such as diopside and augite. Also called TABULAR SPAR.

wood opal. A form of common opal which has replaced pieces of wood entombed as fossils in sediments, in some cases retaining the original structure.

wood tin. A botryoidal or reniform variety of cassiterite which, when broken across, shows a concentric structure of radiating fibres, brown in colour and resembling wood.

wulfenite. Molybdate of lead, $PbMoO_4$, occurring commonly as yellow tetragonal crystals in veins with other lead ores.

wurtzite. Sulphide of zinc, ZnS, of the

same composition as sphalerite, but crystallising in the hexagonal system, in black hemimorphic, pyramidal crystals.

X

xalostockite. A pale rose-pink grossularite which occurs embedded in white marble at Xalostock in Mexico.

xanthosiderite. A hydrated oxide of iron, $Fe_2O_3 \cdot 2H_2O$, occurring as fine yellow or brown needle-like crystals or as an ochre, in association with other oxidic iron ores; of limited distribution.

xenocryst. A single crystal or mineral grain which has been incorporated by magma during its uprise and which therefore occurs as an inclusion in igneous rocks, usually surrounded by reaction rims and more or less corroded by the magma. Cf. XENOLITH.

xenolith. A fragment of rock of extraneous origin which has been incorporated in magma, either intrusive or extrusive, and occurs as an inclusion, often showing definite signs of modification by the magma.

xenomorphic. A textural term implying that the minerals in a rock do not show their own characteristic shapes, but are without regular form by reason of mutual interference.

xenomorphic granular texture. See GRANITOID TEXTURE.

xenotime. Yttrium phosphate, YPO_4, often containing small quantities of cerium, erbium, and thorium, closely resembling zircon in crystal form and general appearance, and occurring in the same types of igneous rock, i.e. in granites and pegmatites as an accessory mineral.

Y

yellow copper ore. A little-used, popular name for CHALCOPYRITE.

yellow quartz. See CITRINE.

yellow tellurium. SYLVANITE.

yenite. ILVAITE.

yttrocerite. A massive, granular or earthy mineral, essentially fluoride of calcium, with the metals of the yttrium and cerium groups, commonly violet-blue in colour, and of rare occurrence.

yttrotantalite. An orthorhombic mineral the name of which conveys the essential chemical composition, though niobium, cerium, yttrium, and calcium are present in varying amounts. At the type-locality, Ytterby (Sweden), it occurs in red feldspar.

yu-stone. Yu or yu-shih, the Chinese name for jade of gemstone quality.

Z

zaratite or **emerald nickel.** A hydrated basic nickel carbonate, occurring as emerald green stalactitic or mammillary masses encrusting crystals of chromite and magnetite at Unst (Shetland Is.), etc.

zeolites. A group of alumino-silicates of sodium, potassium, calcium, and barium, containing very loosely held water, which can be removed by heating and regained by exposure to a moist atmosphere, without destroying the crystal structure. They occur in geodes in igneous rocks, and in red clay, and include chabazite, natrolite, mesolite, stilbite, heulandite, harmotome, phillipsite, etc.

zinc blende. See BLENDE.

zinc bloom. HYDROZINCITE.

zinc spinel. See SPINEL.

zincite. Oxide of zinc, crystallising in the hexagonal system and exhibiting polar symmetry; occurring rarely as crystals, usually as deep-red masses; an important ore of zinc, known also as RED OXIDE OF ZINC, SPARTALITE, and STERLINGITE.

zinkenite. A steel-grey mineral, essentially sulphide of lead and antimony, $PbSb_2S_4$, occurring in antimony-mines at Wolfsberg in the Harz Mountains, in Colorado, and in Arkansas as columnar orthorhombic crystals, sometimes exceptionally thin, forming fibrous masses.

zinkosite. Anhydrous zinc sulphate, occurring at a mine in the Sierra Almagrera (Spain).

zinnwaldite. A variety of mica related in composition to lepidolite (i.e. containing lithium and potassium) but including iron as an essential constituent; occurring in association with tinstone ores at Zinnwald (Erzgebirge), in Cornwall, etc.

zircon. A mineral in tetragonal crystals widely distributed in igneous and sedimentary rocks, and occurring in three forms differing in density and optical characters. It varies in colour from brown to green, blue, red, golden-yellow, while colourless zircons make particularly brilliant stones when cut and polished. In composition it is essentially silicate of zirconium, though green specimens contain amorphous silica and zirconia. A small amount of the rare element hafnium is present. See also JACINTH, JARGON, MATURA DIAMOND, CEYLONESE ZIRCON.

zoisite. Hydrated alumino-silicate of calcium, crystallising in the orthorhombic system and occurring chiefly in metamorphic schists; also a constituent of so-called saussurite. Clino-zoisite is of the same composition, but crystallises in the monoclinic system.

zoning. Concentric layering parallel to the periphery of a crystalline mineral, shown by colour banding in such minerals as tourmaline, and by differences of the optical reactions to polarised light in colourless minerals like feldspars.

zunyite. A rare basic orthosilicate of aluminium, containing fluorine and chlorine; it occurs in minute cubic crystals at the Zuñi mine, Silverton, Colorado.

Edinburgh: Printed by T. and A. CONSTABLE LTD.

1, Diamond. 2, Graphite. 3, Sulphur.

A

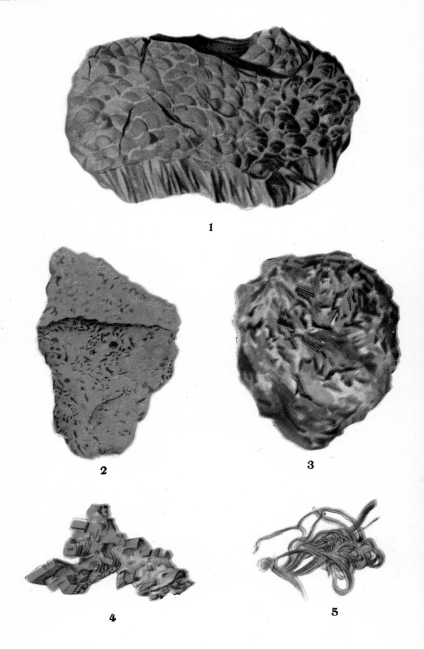

1, Arsenic. 2, Antimony. 3, Bismuth. 4, 5, Silver.

1, Platinum. 2—4, Gold. 5, 6, Copper.

1, 2, Stibnite.   3, 4, Realgar and Orpiment.

1, Molybdenite. 2, Zinc-blende. 3, 4, Galena.

1, Niccolite.   2, 3, Cinnabar.   4, Mispickel.

1, Marcasite.   2, 3, Iron-pyrites.   4, Pyrrhotite.

1, 2, Copper-pyrites.   3, Smaltite.   4, Tetrahedrite.   5, Pyrargyrite.   6, Proustite.

1

2

1, 2, Fluor-spar.

1, 2, Rock-salt.   3, Atacamite.   4, 5, Opal

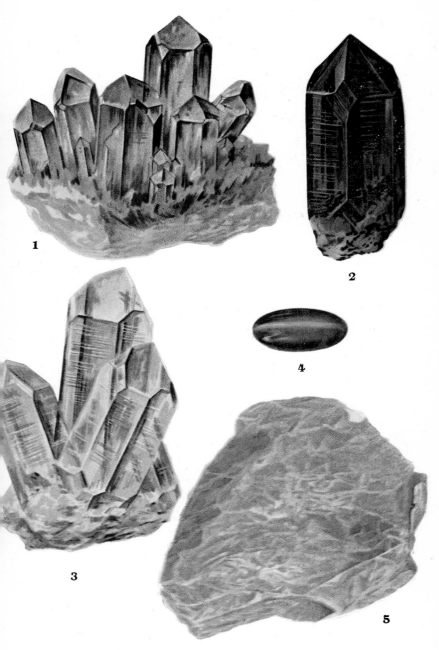

Amethyst. 2, Smoky-quartz. 3, Rock-crystal. 4, Cat's-eye. 5, Rose-quartz.

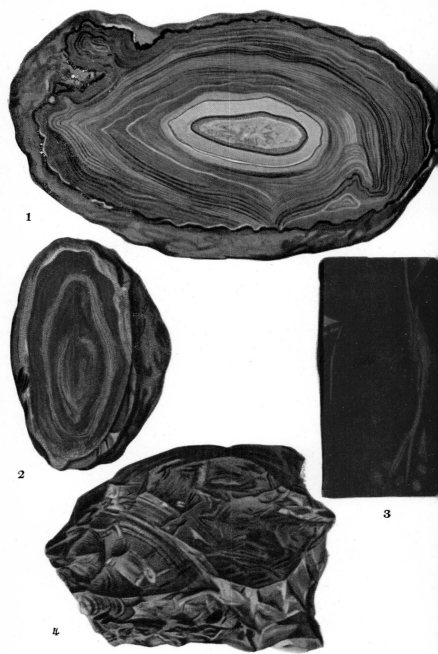

1, Agate.   2, 3, Jasper.   4, Hornstone.

1—4, Haematite.

1, Magnetite. 2, Corundum. 3, Cassiterite. 4, Zircon. 5, Pitchblende. 6, Limonite.

1, Manganite.   2, 3, Pyrolusite.   4, Psilomelane.

1—3, Calcite.

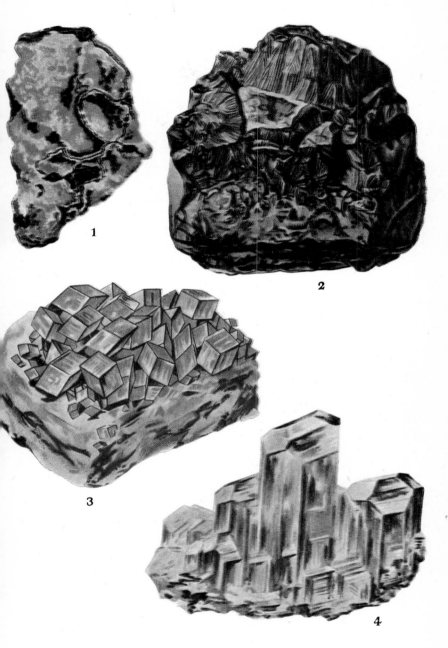

1, Calamine.   2, Chalybite   3, Rhodochrosite.   4. Cerussite.

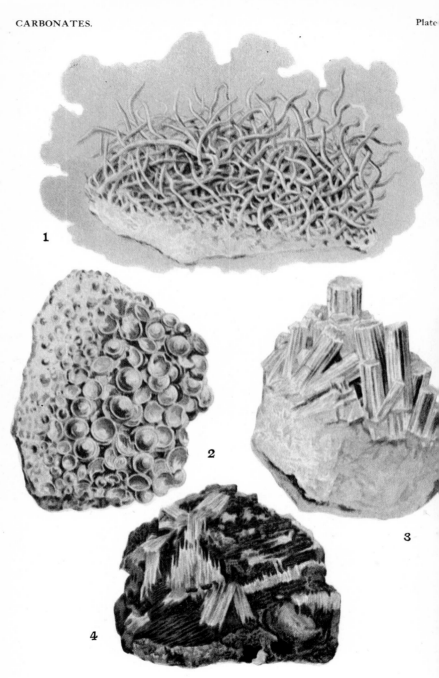

1—3, Aragonite. 4, Cerussite.

1, 2, Chessylite.   3, 4, Malachite.

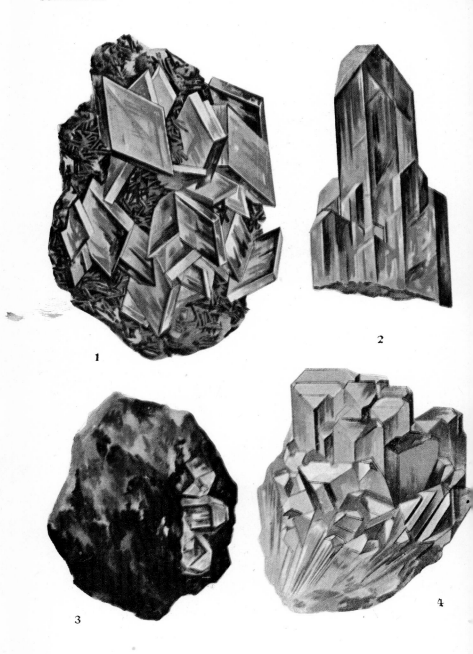

1, 2, Barytes. 3, Anglesite. 4, Celestite.

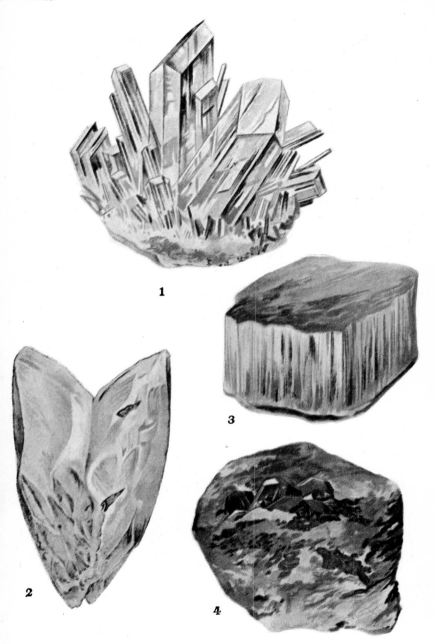

1—3, Gypsum.   4, Linarite.

1, Crocoite.   2, Wolframite.   3, Wulfenite.   4, Scheelite.

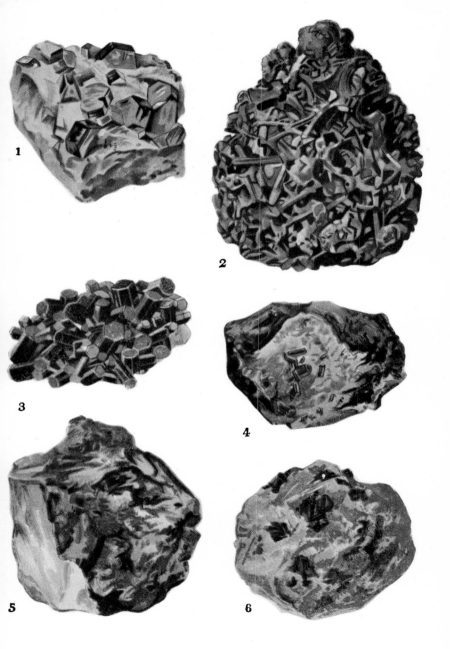

1, Apatite. 2, 3, Pyromorphite. 4, Vanadinite. 5, 6, Erythrite.

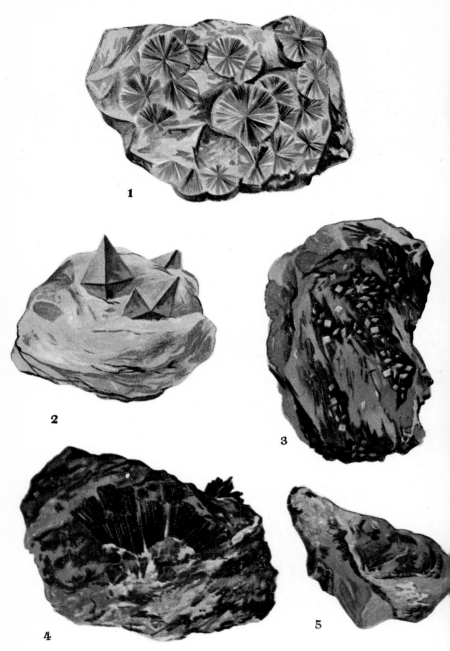

1, Wavellite.   2, Lazulite.   3, Cuprouranite.   4, Vivianite.   5, Turquoise.

1, 2, Orthoclase.   3, Labradorite.   4, Microcline.   5, Anorthite.

1, Hornblende. 2, Actinolite. 3, Crocidolite. 4, Nephrite.

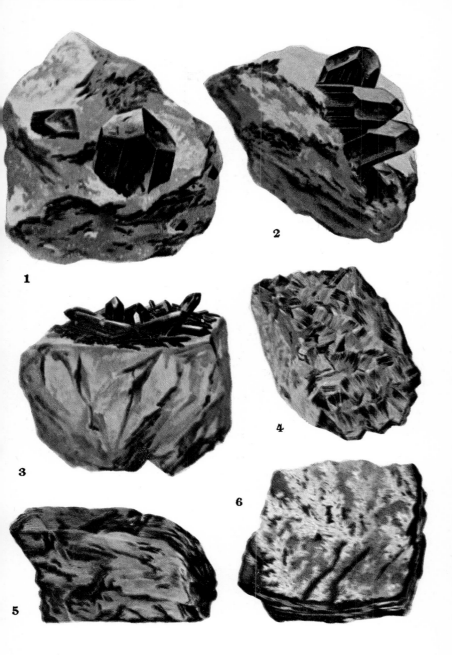

1, Augite. 2, 3, Diopside. 4, Bronzite. 5, Hypersthene. 6, Wollastonite.

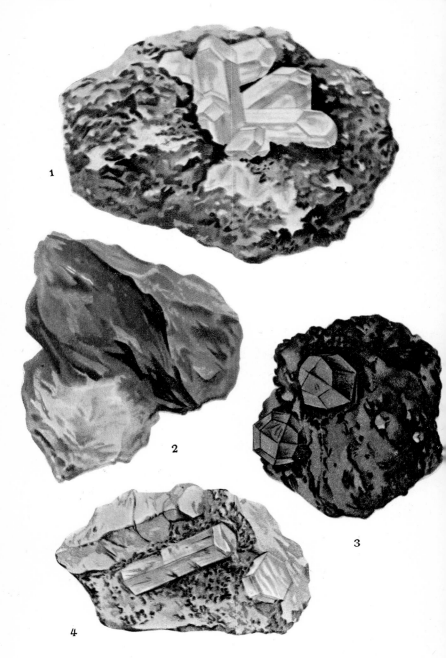

1, Sodalite. 2, Lapis-luzuli. 3, Leucite. 4, Beryl.

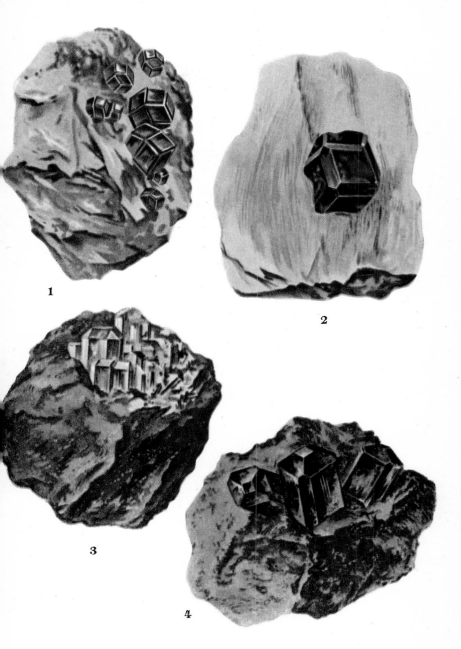

1, 2, Garnet. 3, Olivine. 4, Idocrase.

1

2

1, 2, Topaz.

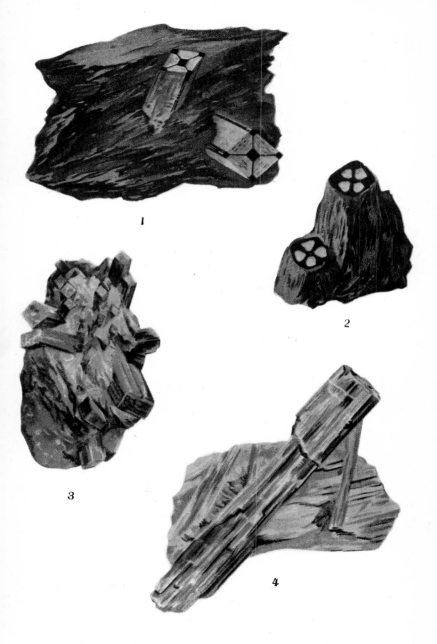

1—3, Andalusite (1—2, var. Chiastolite).   4, Kyanite.

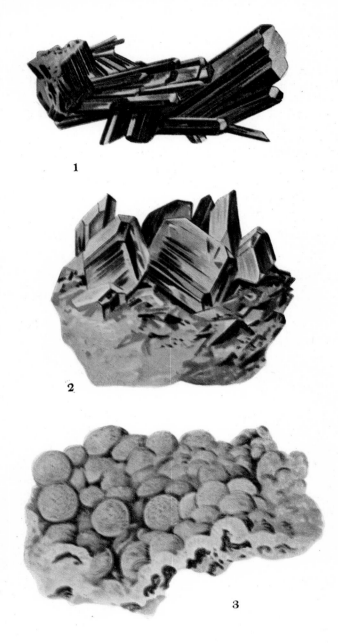

1, Epidote. 2 Axinite. 3, Prehnite.

1—3, Tourmaline. 4, 5, Staurolite.

1, Muscovite.   2, Biotite.   3, Zinnwaldite.   4, Clinochlore.   5, Lepidolite.

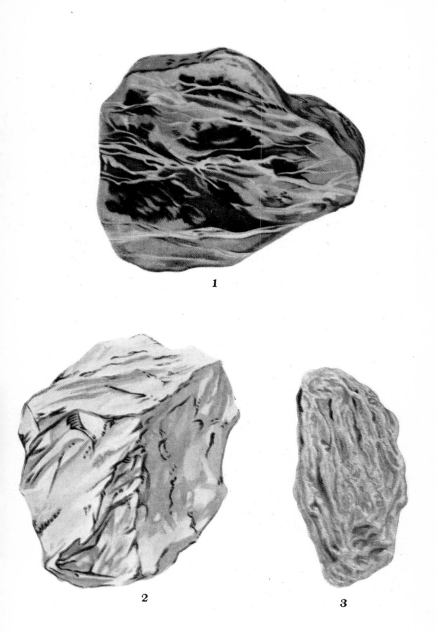

1, Serpentine.   2, Meerschaum.   3, Talc.

1

2

1, Analcite.   2, Chabazite.

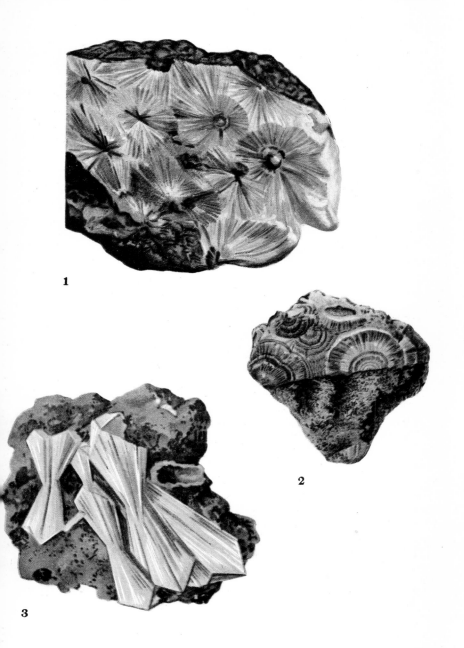

1, 2, Natrolite.   3, Stilbite.

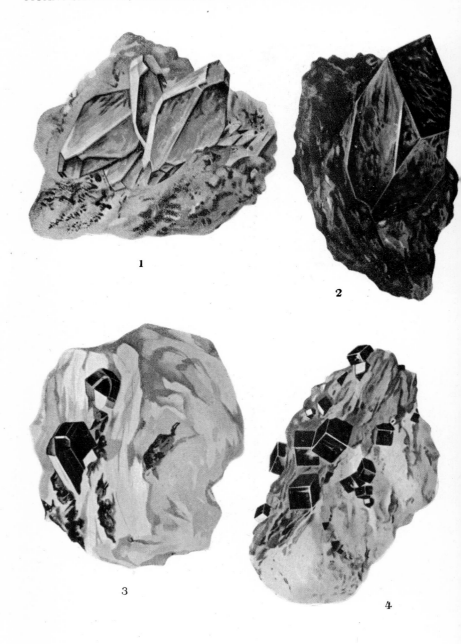

1, 2, Sphene.   3, Columbite.   4, Perovskite.

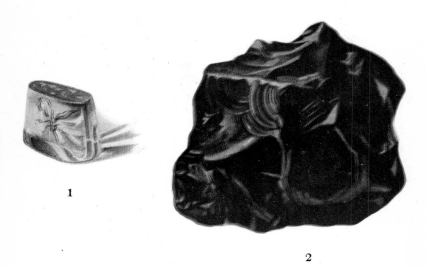

1

2

3

1, Amber (enclosing insect). 2, Asphaltum. 3, Lignite.

1

2

1, Coal.   2, Anthracite.